W9-CZT-814

WITHDRAWN

BASIC SERVOMECHANISMS

ED BUKSTEIN

Instructor in Advanced Electronics
Northwestern Television and Electronics Institute

BASIC
SERVOMECHANISMS

HOLT, RINEHART AND WINSTON
New York - Chicago - San Francisco
Toronto - London

The servomechanism is a self-correcting control system. An error-detecting device compares the output of the system against a reference input to determine whether or not the system output is at the desired value. In the event that it is not, the error detector produces a signal which is amplified and applied to an error-correcting device. The corrector then restores the output to the desired value. This technique of automatic control is not new, but it has received greater attention in recent years because of its increased usage in industrial and military apparatus. In industry, servomechanisms have accelerated the trend toward automation, increasing production rates and reducing production costs. In military applications, the servomechanism is a basic building block of automatic flight controls and missile guidance systems.

Basic Servomechanisms is addressed to the level of the electronics technician. Emphasis is therefore largely on principles of operation rather than on design factors and procedures. Chapter 1 is introductory in nature, dealing with the basic concept of the closed-loop control system. This chapter establishes the frame of reference for the remainder of the book. Chapters 2, 3, and 4 are devoted to error-detecting devices: potentiometers, transducers, and synchros, respectively. Chapter 5 deals with error correctors. Vacuum tubes, transistors, magnetic amplifiers, and rotary amplifiers are all used extensively in servomechanism equipment, and these are discussed in Chapters 6, 7, 8, and 9. Stabilization techniques are covered in Chapter 10, and practical applications of servomechanisms are described in Chapter 11.

ED BUKSTEIN

Minneapolis, Minn.
September, 1962

CONTENTS

Closed-loop Control Systems

CHAPTER 1

1-1. INTRODUCTION

Automatic controls are used extensively in industrial, commercial, and military applications. These controls vary widely in circuit design and in degree of complexity according to such requirements as accuracy, stability, and speed of response. An automatic temperature controller, for example, may be relatively simple in design, while a system for controlling the flight path of an aircraft or a missile may be extremely complex.

In one important class of automatic controls, known as *feedback control systems*, feedback is employed to compare the controlled quantity against a reference quantity. Such comparison determines whether or not the controlled quantity (temperature, pressure, fluid flow rate, mechanical position, and so forth) is at the desired value. In the event that the controlled quantity is at some value other than the desired one, the comparison device produces an *error signal*. This signal is amplified and used to restore the controlled quantity to the desired value. In this manner the system seeks to reduce the error signal to zero, at which time the controlled quantity will be at the desired value.

A *servomechanism* is a feedback control system in which the controlled quantity is *mechanical position* (although the term "servomechanism" is often used loosely to describe any feedback control system). Position-control servomechanisms are commonly used in such applications as controlling the rudder of a ship, the elevators and other flight control surfaces of an aircraft, the setting of a valve

/ **1**

in a fuel line, the position of an automatic-tracking radar antenna, and so forth.

1-2. OPEN-LOOP CONTROL SYSTEM

In an open-loop control system, the output quantity (pressure, motor speed, temperature, and so forth) can be adjusted to the desired value, but there is no automatic compensation to correct the output when it deviates from the desired value. As an example of an open-loop control system, consider a motor control circuit employing a variable resistor in series with the armature of the motor. By means of this variable resistor, the armature input can be adjusted to make the motor rotate at the desired number of revolutions per minute. Setting the variable resistor to the required number of ohms, however, will provide no assurance that the motor will continue to rotate at the desired number of revolutions per minute. The motor may speed up or slow down as a result of changes of supply voltage or variations of mechanical loading on the motor shaft. Such changes will not initiate automatic corrective action to restore the motor to the desired speed. There is no feedback by means of which the output (speed) can be compared against a reference quantity. The variable resistor can control the speed of the motor, but the motor cannot control the setting of the variable resistor.

1-3. CLOSED-LOOP CONTROL SYSTEM

The simple motor speed control described above can be converted to a closed-loop system by modifying it in such a way that a change of motor speed will cause a change in the setting of the variable resistor. A change of motor speed will then produce a change of armature input, restoring the motor to the desired speed. One way of accomplishing this result is illustrated in Fig. 1-1. A small d-c generator is mechanically coupled to the shaft of the motor so that the output voltage of the generator is a function of motor speed: the generator produces less voltage when the motor slows down, and more voltage when the motor speeds up. The output voltage of the generator is applied to a solenoid, and the movable iron core of the solenoid is mechanically coupled to the slider of the variable resistor. A spring tends to pull this slider in one direction, and the solenoid tends to pull it in the opposite direction. The slider therefore moves to a position at which the spring tension is exactly balanced by the force of the solenoid. Now, if the motor tends to speed up, the generator will apply more voltage to the solenoid. The iron core will be drawn farther into the solenoid coil, and the slider of the variable resistor will move until the spring tension has increased to balance the new value of force exerted by the solenoid. This movement of the slider increases the resistance in series with the armature of the motor. As a result, the motor slows down and is restored to the original speed. If the motor speed should tend to decrease below the desired value, less voltage will be applied to the solenoid. The slider of the variable resistor will now move in the direction that causes an increase of armature input, and the motor speed will increase until it reaches the desired value.

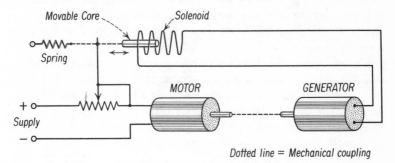

Fig. 1-1 Closed-Loop Control

The control system illustrated in Fig. 1-1 has some disadvantages that would limit its performance. Better performance characteristics can be achieved by using the generator to control the bias of a thyratron rectifier supplying the input to the armature of the motor. Fig. 1-1 does, however, illustrate the requirement of a closed-loop control system: that a change of output (motor speed) will cause a change of input (armature excitation) to restore the output to its original value.

1-4. SERVOMECHANISM PRINCIPLES

A servomechanism is a closed-loop control system in which the output (controlled quantity) is mechanical position. The evolution of a servomechanism is illustrated in Fig. 1-2. Here, the output quantity to be controlled is the position of an antenna. By closing the switch in the circuit shown in Fig. 1-2(A), an operator can rotate the antenna. When the antenna has reached the desired position, the operator opens the switch to stop the motor. This simple control system has many disadvantages:

1. The operator may not open the switch soon enough and the antenna will move beyond the desired position (overshoot).

2. The motor is not reversible in direction. If the antenna overshoots the desired position, it must be rotated "all the way around" to get back to the desired position again.

3. The antenna may be located out of sight of the operator (outside or on the roof of the building, for example). If there is no remote indicator to display antenna position, the operator must "estimate" the position of the antenna. Knowing the motor speed and the reduction ratio of the gear box, the operator must close the switch for the length of time that would be required to bring the antenna to the desired position. This required length of time depends on motor speed, but the motor speed may change due to supply voltage variations. Such a system of *dead reckoning* is therefore highly inaccurate. Human errors on the part of the operator also contribute to total inaccuracy. Another disadvantage of this system is that the operator must know the "last" position of the antenna in order to rotate it to a new position. All of these errors are cumulative so that, after several changes of position, the total error may be considerable.

Fig. 1-2(B) shows an improved version of the circuit of Fig. 1-2(A). Here, a reversible motor is used so that in the event the antenna overshoots, the operator can "back it up" to the desired position. One field of the motor is connected to the power lines through a phase-shifting capacitor, and the other field is connected through a two-pole, three-position switch. By means of this switch, the operator can reverse the phase of the voltage applied to one of the fields, causing the motor to reverse its direction of rotation. Except that the motor is reversible, this circuit has the same limitations as that of Fig. 1-2(A).

The circuits in Figs. 1-2(A) and 1-2(B) are both of the *on-off* type: the motor is either on or off and there is no provision for varying the speed of rotation. Fig. 1-2(C) represents a further improvement because it permits control of speed as well as direction of rotation. The two voltage dividers, one with a fixed tap and the other

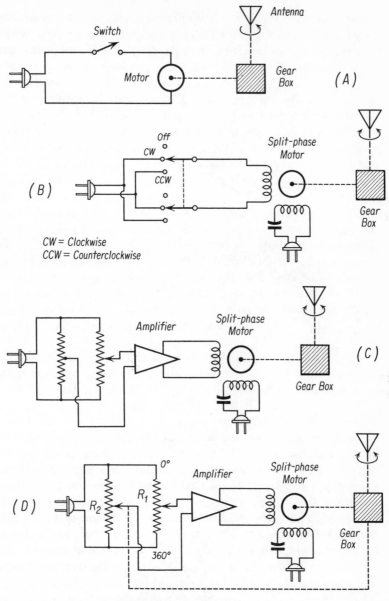

Fig. 1-2 The Servomechanism

variable, constitute a bridge circuit. When the slider is at a position corresponding to that of the fixed tap (center of the resistance element), the bridge is balanced and there is no input to the amplifier.

Under these conditions, the amplifier produces no output and the motor does not rotate. If the slider is now moved away from its center position, the bridge will be unbalanced and will supply an input to the amplifier. Since the amplifier now produces output, the motor rotates. The direction of rotation is determined by the direction in which the slider has been moved away from its center position. Moving the slider upward from center will unbalance the bridge in one direction, and moving it downward will unbalance the circuit in the opposite direction. Moving the slider from one side of center to the other reverses the phase of the input signal to the amplifier. The output of the amplifier also reverses in phase, changing the direction of rotation of the motor.

The speed of rotation of the motor is determined by the extent to which the slider has been moved away from its center position. If the slider is moved only slightly away from center, the bridge will be only slightly unbalanced. The amplifier therefore receives a small amplitude signal and the motor rotates slowly. If the slider had been moved farther away from center, the bridge would have become unbalanced to a greater extent. With a greater amplitude of input signal to the amplifier, the motor would have rotated faster.

With the circuit arrangement shown in Fig. 1-2(C), the operator can slow down the motor as the antenna approaches the desired position. This feature helps to prevent overshoot, but control is still basically of the *dead reckoning* type. The circuits of Figs. 1-2(A), 1-2(B), and 1-2(C) are all of the open-loop variety: there is no provision for automatic corrective action to restore the output (antenna position) when it deviates from the desired value.

A further improvement is illustrated in Fig. 1-2(D). Here, the motor is mechanically coupled to the shaft of one of the potentiometers. In practice, this potentiometer would be mounted near the motor or antenna structure to simplify the mechanical coupling. Since the bridge circuit can control the motor and the motor can control the bridge, this is a closed-loop, self-correcting system.

If the antenna in Fig. 1-2(D) is not in the desired position, the bridge is unbalanced and the motor rotates. As the motor rotates, it turns the antenna and also the shaft of the potentiometer to which it is mechanically coupled. Rotation of the motor continues until the bridge has been restored to a balanced condition. At this time the motor stops and the antenna is now in the desired position. The circuit is therefore *self-balancing* or *null-seeking*. Each time the operator moves the slider of potentiometer R_1, the motor rotates and turns the shaft of R_2 (as well as the antenna). In this manner, the slider of R_2 automatically follows the motion of the slider of R_1. Potentiometer R_1 can be fitted with a dial calibrated from 0 to 360 deg to represent the bearing (azimuth) of the antenna. The antenna will automatically rotate to the direction indicated by the dial setting. Since this is a closed-loop control system in which the output quantity is mechanical position, this is a *true* servomechanism.

An important feature of the circuit shown in Fig. 1-2(D) is that the motor slows down as the antenna approaches the desired position (because the bridge approaches balance and supplies less input to the amplifier). The rate of correction is therefore proportional to the amount of error. Such proportional control helps to reduce overshoot.

1-5. SERVOMECHANISM COMPONENTS

A generalized block diagram of a servomechanism is shown in Fig. 1-3. As indicated, the complete servomechanism consists of three basic, functional components: an error detector, an amplifier, and an error corrector. The error detector is a comparison device which compares the output against the reference input. In the event that the output is not at the desired value (represented by the reference input), the error detector produces an error signal. This error signal is then amplified and applied to the error corrector. The error corrector, in turn, supplies the force required to restore the output to the desired value. When this has been accomplished, the feedback (representing the output) is equal to the reference input (representing the desired value of output). Under these conditions, the error detector produces no output and the error corrector is *at rest*. In a

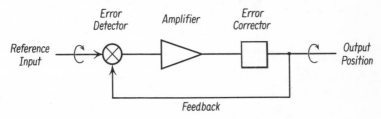

Fig. 1-3 Block Diagram of Servomechanism

sense, the error detector is the "brain" of the system and determines when corrective action is necessary. The error corrector is the "muscle" of the system and supplies the force required to correct the output.

Error Detectors

In the circuit shown in Fig. 1-2(D), the two potentiometers of the bridge circuit comprise the error detector. The position of the slider of R_1 is the reference input and represents the desired position of the output (antenna). The mechanical coupling to R_2 constitutes the feedback and represents the actual position of the output. Whenever the actual position of the output differs from the desired position, the sliders of R_1 and R_2 will be at different potentials. This difference is the error signal and is applied to the amplifier. The motor in Fig. 1-2(D) functions as the error corrector and supplies the force to move the output to the desired position (simultaneously restoring the bridge to a condition of balance).

Error detectors of many types are available and are selected according to the requirements of the specific application. These are described in detail in Chapters 2, 3, and 4. Two typical units are shown in Figs. 1-4 and 1-5.

The E transformer illustrated in Fig. 1-4 is a special form of the differential transformer. The E section of the transformer

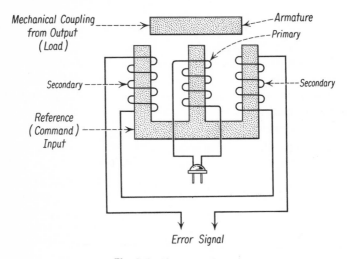

Fig. 1-4 The E Transformer

core has a primary winding on the center leg and two identical secondary windings on the outside legs. The two secondaries are connected series opposing so that their voltages cancel. When the armature section of the core is exactly centered over the E section, the same amount of voltage will be induced in the two secondaries. Under these conditions, the secondary voltages will exactly cancel and there will be no error output voltage. If, however, the armature is not centered over the E section, the coupling to one secondary will be greater than the coupling to the other. More voltage will now be induced in one secondary than is induced in the other. Since the two secondary voltages no longer exactly cancel, an error voltage equal to the difference appears at the output terminals. The magnitude of this error voltage will be proportional to the amount the armature has been moved away from its center position. The phase of the error signal is determined by the direction in which the armature has been moved away from center.

In practice, the E transformer may be mounted so that both the armature and the E section are movable. The armature may be mechanically coupled to the load to represent the actual value of the output. The movable E section represents the reference input and can be moved to the position representing the desired position of the load. Whenever the actual position of the load differs from the desired position, the armature will not be centered over the E section. The resulting error signal is amplified and used to move the load to the desired position. This movement is mechanically coupled to the armature. When the armature reaches its center position, the error signal is zero and the load stops moving.

An error detector employing *synchros*[1] is shown in Fig. 1-5. The synchro, which resembles a small motor in appearance, contains a rotor winding and three Y-connected stator windings. The rotor of the synchro transmitter is connected to an a-c source and functions as a primary winding. Voltage is therefore induced in the stator windings which function as secondaries. The amount of voltage induced in each stator winding depends upon the physical position of the rotor winding with respect to the stator. Since the position of the rotor can be changed by turning the shaft of the synchro, the amount of voltage induced in the stator windings can be changed. For any given position of the rotor shaft, there is a corresponding set

---

[1] The synchro is often referred to as a *selsyn* (trade name of General Electric Co.).

of voltages induced in the stator windings. In the synchro control transformer, the stator windings function as a primary and the rotor as a secondary. The amount of voltage induced in the rotor depends upon the physical position of the rotor with respect to the stator windings.

As shown in Fig. 1-5, the shaft (rotor) position of the synchro transmitter represents the reference input. The shaft of the control transformer represents the output. Since the secondary (stator) voltages of the transmitter are applied as primary (stator) voltage to the control transformer, the amount of voltage induced in the rotor of the control transformer depends upon the position of

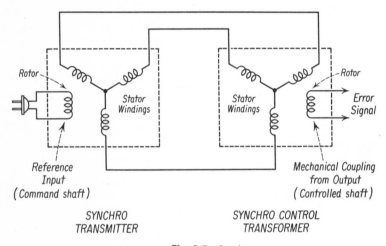

Fig. 1-5 Synchros

the rotor of the transmitter. The voltage induced in the rotor of the control transformer is the error signal, and the magnitude of this voltage depends upon the angular difference between the two rotors. This error signal is amplified and applied to a motor. The motor positions the load (output) and also turns the shaft of the control transformer. When this rotor reaches a position corresponding to the position of the transmitter rotor, the error signal is zero. At this time the motor stops and the load is in the desired position. The reference input shaft, also known as the *command shaft,* can be fitted with a calibrated dial and can be set to represent the desired position of the load. Each time the command shaft is moved, the load will be repositioned accordingly.

Servoamplifiers

The amplifier of a servomechanism must have sufficient sensitivity to respond to the low-level signal from the error detector, and must produce sufficient output power to drive the error corrector. Vacuum tube, transistor, and magnetic amplifiers are commonly used in practice. The over-all performance of the servomechanism is dependent upon the characteristics of the servoamplifier, particularly with respect to the gain and frequency response of the amplifier. Since some error detectors produce d-c error signals and others produce a-c signals, the amplifier must be suitable for the type

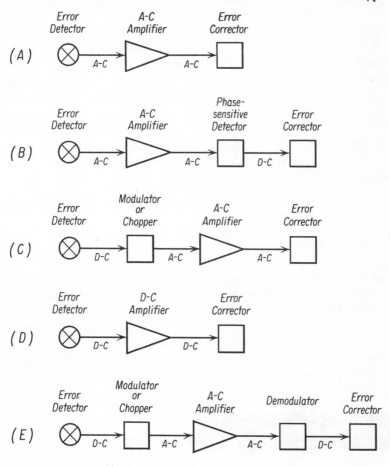

Fig. 1-6 Servomechanism Variations

of signal produced by the error detector with which it is to be used. In addition, the error corrector may require either a-c or d-c input depending upon its design.

Fig. 1-6(A) shows an error detector which produces an a-c error signal, and an error corrector requiring an a-c input. An a-c amplifier (*R-C* or transformer coupled) is therefore employed. In Fig. 1-6(B), the error signal is alternating current but the error corrector requires a d-c input. The output of the amplifier is therefore applied to a phase-sensitive detector which converts the a-c signal to a d-c voltage whose polarity is determined by the phase of the alternating current. In Fig. 1-6(C), the error signal is direct current but the error corrector requires an a-c input. A *modulator* or *chopper* is therefore used to convert the d-c error signal to alternating current. When the error signal is direct current and the error corrector requires d-c input, a d-c (direct-coupled) amplifier may be used as shown in Fig. 1-6(D). Because d-c amplifiers present design problems more severe than those of a-c amplifiers, a-c amplifiers are preferred by many designers. The arrangement shown in Fig. 1-6(E) is therefore often used in preference to the one shown in Fig. 1-6(D). The modulator or chopper converts the d-c error signal to alternating current, permitting the use of an a-c amplifier. The output signal of the amplifier is then demodulated to produce the d-c input required by the error corrector.

Error Correctors

The error corrector of a servomechanism must provide the mechanical force to position the load. Electric motors (both a-c and d-c), solenoids, and electrically operated valves are frequently used as error correctors. In addition to its ability to supply the necessary mechanical force, the error corrector must also be capable of sufficient speed of response to satisfy the requirements of the application in which it is used. Gear trains, cams, and other forms of mechanical coupling are often used in conjunction with the error corrector. These transmit the mechanical motion required to position the load and to rebalance the circuit to a condition of zero error.

SUMMARY

In contrast to an open-loop control system, a closed-loop system is self-correcting. When the output of a closed-loop system deviates from the desired value, the circuit responds to this change and restores the output to the correct value. This self-restoration of the output is accomplished by means of feedback (either mechanical, electrical, or both). The feedback, representing the actual value of output, is compared to a reference input representing the desired value of output. As a consequence of this comparison, the error detector produces an output signal representing the difference between the actual and desired values of output. This error signal is amplified and applied to an error corrector. As the corrector restores the output to the desired value, the error signal is reduced to zero and the corrective action stops.

The servomechanism is a closed-loop, feedback control system in which the controlled output is mechanical position. Typical applications include positioning of radar antennas and of control surfaces of aircraft and missiles.

According to its design, the error detector may produce an a-c or a d-c output. The servoamplifier must be designed accordingly and must supply the type of output (a-c or d-c) required by the error corrector.

QUESTIONS

1. Explain the difference between open-loop and closed-loop control systems.
2. What is the purpose of the *reference input* in a feedback control system?
3. Is the error signal the *input* or the *output* of an error detector?
4. What two quantities are compared in the error detector?
5. Sketch an *E* transformer and explain its operation.
6. Under what conditions is a chopper used in a servomechanism?
7. Under what conditions is a demodulator used in a servomechanism?
8. What is meant by *overshoot*?

Error Detectors: Potentiometers

CHAPTER 2

2-1. D-C POTENTIOMETER BRIDGE

The error detector of a servomechanism produces an error signal when there is a difference between the actual value of output and the desired value. In some servomechanism designs, the magnitude of the error signal is proportional to the difference between actual and desired output. In other designs, the error signal is proportional to the rate at which the output is deviating from the desired value. In still others, an error signal is produced only when the output has deviated by a predetermined amount. In all of these variations however, the basic function of the error detector is the same: to produce an error signal which will initiate a corrective action in the system.

The potentiometer is used extensively as an error-detecting device. Connected as a bridge circuit, as shown in Fig. 2-1, a pair of potentiometers will produce an error voltage whose magnitude is dependent upon the difference in position of the two sliders. If the slider of the right-hand potentiometer is positioned closer to the positive terminal of the supply than the slider of the left-hand potentiometer, the error voltage will be of positive polarity with respect to ground. The magnitude of this positive error voltage depends upon the amount of difference in the positions of the two sliders: the greater the difference, the greater the error voltage. The numerical relationships are illustrated in Fig. 2-1(A). Here, it is assumed that (1) the supply voltage is 100 v, (2) both potentiometers are linear, and (3) the amplifier to which the error voltage is applied has negli-

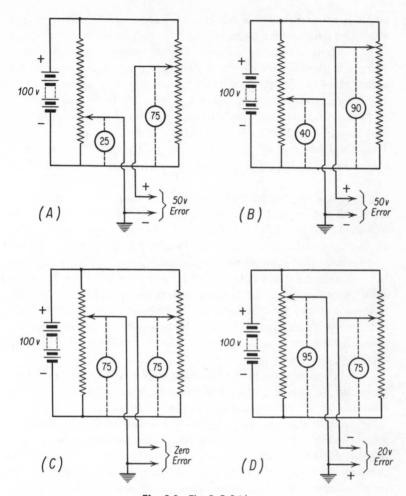

Fig. 2-1 The D-C Bridge

gible loading effect on the bridge circuit. If the slider of the left-hand potentiometer is positioned one-quarter of the way up on its resistance element, it will be at a potential of 25 v with respect to the negative terminal of the supply. If the slider of the right-hand potentiometer is positioned three-quarters of the way up on its resistance element, it will be at a potential of 75 v with respect to the negative terminal of the supply. Under these conditions, the difference of potential between the two sliders will be 50 v, the right-hand slider being positive with respect to the left-hand one. Since the left-hand slider is grounded, a positive error voltage of 50 v will appear at the output terminals of the bridge.

It is of interest to note that the magnitude of the error voltage is determined by the *difference* of position of the sliders rather than by the absolute positions. In Fig. 2-1(B), for example, the error is also 50 v with respect to ground. Here, the left-hand slider is positioned four-tenths of the way up the resistance element, and the right-hand slider is nine-tenths of the way up on its element. Even though the absolute positions of the sliders differ from those shown in Fig. 2-1(A), the difference of position is the same in both cases.

If the left-hand slider in Fig. 2-1(A) is gradually moved upward, the positive error voltage will gradually decrease in amplitude. When the left-hand slider has reached a position equivalent to that of the right-hand slider, as shown in Fig. 2-1(C), the error voltage will be zero; that is, there will be no difference of potential between the two sliders. If the left-hand slider is moved still farther in an upward direction, an error voltage will again appear at the output terminals of the bridge. Since the right-hand slider is now closer to the negative terminal of the supply than is the left-hand slider, the error signal is of negative polarity. This condition is illustrated in Fig. 2-1(D).

For illustration, the left-hand sliders in Fig. 2-1 are shown grounded. In practice, this point might be left ungrounded, but the relative potentials and polarities would still be the same.

A servomechanism employing a d-c potentiometer bridge is shown in Fig. 2-2. The error voltage applied to the amplifier has a magnitude and polarity determined by the relative positions of the command shaft and the follow-up shaft. Depending on whether the error voltage is positive or negative, the motor will rotate in one direction or the other. The mechanical coupling to the follow-up shaft is such that the shaft rotates in a direction that reduces the magnitude of the error voltage. When the follow-up shaft has reached an angular position corresponding to that of the command shaft, the error voltage will be zero and the motor will stop. Since the response time of the circuit can be made relatively short, the follow-up shaft will almost instantly follow any movement of the command shaft.

The output (controlled) shaft in Fig. 2-2 can be coupled to the load to be positioned, and a dial can be attached to the command shaft. The load will then automatically assume the position to

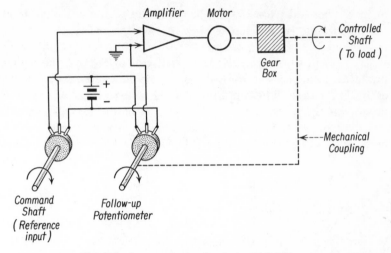

Fig. 2-2 Servomechanism Employing D-C Bridge

which the command shaft is dialed. Furthermore, the load will maintain this position because any deviation will produce an error signal and will initiate a corrective action. This type of remote positioning is often used to control radar antennas, searchlights, and so forth.

2-2. A-C POTENTIOMETER BRIDGE

In Figs. 2-1 and 2-2, a d-c source of bridge excitation voltage is shown, and the output of the bridge (error) is therefore a d-c potential. To amplify this error voltage, a d-c (direct-coupled) amplifier is required. Alternatively, a chopper may be used to convert the d-c error voltage to a corresponding a-c signal. An a-c amplifier (*R-C* or transformer coupled) may now be used. This alternative is often preferred, even though it requires the use of a chopper circuit, because d-c amplifiers tend to be unstable with respect to supply voltage and temperature variations.

In Fig. 2-3, a-c excitation is used for the bridge circuit. This permits the use of an a-c amplifier and eliminates the need of a chopper. If the potentiometers are wire-wound, however, as they often are in practice, they will present an inductive as well as a resistive component to the excitation frequency. This inductive component, if appreciable, will adversely affect the accuracy of the servomechanism in which the bridge is used. Since excitation frequency is generally low (60 to 1,000 cps), the inductive reactance of the potentiometers is relatively low. A-c bridge excitation is therefore frequently used in practice.

With sine-wave excitation, as shown in Fig. 2-3, the bridge produces a sine-wave error voltage of the same frequency as the excitation source. The amplitude of the sine-wave error signal is dependent upon the difference of position of the two sliders, and the phase of the error signal is determined by the relative positions of the sliders. The error signal will be either *in phase* or *180 deg out*

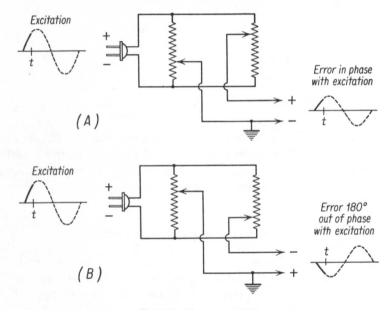

Fig. 2-3 The A-C Bridge

of phase with the excitation, depending upon the direction in which the bridge is unbalanced.

Fig. 2-3(A) shows the relative polarities of bridge input and output at an instant of time (*t*) during the positive half-cycle of input. Since the right-hand slider is closer to the power line that is positive at time *t*, the ungrounded output terminal is also positive at this time. A positive half-cycle of error signal is therefore produced during the positive half-cycle of input; that is, the error signal is *in phase* with the excitation. If the right-hand slider had been closer to the opposite power line, as shown in Fig. 2-3(B), the ungrounded output terminal would be negative at time *t*. Since a nega-

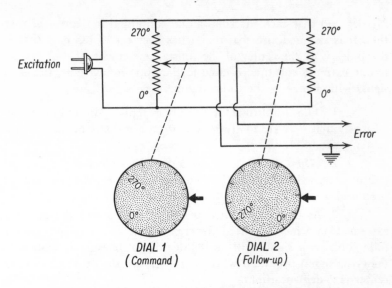

DIAL 1
(Command)

DIAL 2
(Follow-up)

DIAL 1	DIAL 2	ERROR	ERROR PHASE WITH RESPECT TO EXCITATION
135°	270°		0°
135°	150°		0°
135°	135°		
135°	120°		180°
135°	0°		180°

Fig. 2-4 Comparison of Positions of Shafts

tive half-cycle of error signal appears during the positive half-cycle of excitation, the error signal is 180 deg out of phase with respect to the excitation.

The use of an a-c potentiometer bridge for comparing the angular positions of two shafts is shown in Fig. 2-4. Here, it is assumed that each potentiometer can be rotated through an angle of

270 deg and that each shaft has a dial calibrated in degrees of rotation. It is assumed also that dial 1 has been set to 135 deg; that is, the slider is at the center of the resistance element. If dial 2 is set to one extreme and then rotated to the opposite extreme, the error signal will change in the following manner:

1. The amplitude of the error signal will gradually decrease as dial 2 is gradually moved from one extreme toward the center position (135 deg).

2. When dial 2 reaches 135 deg, the sliders of the two potentiometers will be at equal potentials and no error signal will be produced.

3. As dial 2 is rotated from 135 deg toward the opposite extreme from which it started, the error signal will increase in amplitude. This error signal will be 180 deg out of phase with respect to the error signal produced when dial 2 was on the other side of the center (135-deg) position.

The error signal produced by the bridge in Fig. 2-4 can be amplified and applied to a reversible motor whose direction of rotation is determined by the phase of the driving voltage. The motor will then rotate in one direction if dial 2 reads higher than dial 1, and in the opposite direction if dial 2 reads lower. If the motor is mechanically coupled to the shaft of dial 2, the circuit becomes self-balancing or null-seeking. When the two dials are not at the same setting, an error signal will be produced and the motor will rotate. This rotation, coupled to the shaft of dial 2, will continue until dial 2 reaches the same setting as dial 1. The error signal will then be zero, and the motor will stop. The follow-up dial therefore duplicates any movement of the command dial.

2-3. RESOLUTION

Potentiometers designed for use in servomechanism applications are, in general, of better quality and are manufactured to more exacting specifications than potentiometers designed for use in audio, radio, and television equipment. It is of relatively little importance, for example, that the volume control of an audio amplifier may have to be advanced 75 deg rather than 70 deg to achieve a desired level of volume. By contrast, an error of 5 deg of shaft rotation in a servomechanism is intolerable in most applications.

One of the important characteristics of a potentiometer designed for servomechanism use is its *resolution*. The resolution of a potentiometer is determined by the minimum amount by which the resistance (between the slider and one end of the resistance element) can be changed by rotating the shaft. In wire-wound potentiometers, which are frequently used in servomechanisms, the minimum resistance change is determined by the size of the resistance wire and by the length of each turn. As illustrated in Fig. 2-5, the wire-wound potentiometer is made up of a length of resistance wire wound on an insulated form bent into a semicircular shape. As the shaft of the potentiometer is rotated, the slider moves in succession from one turn of wire to the next. If the slider in Fig. 2-5 is moved from turn

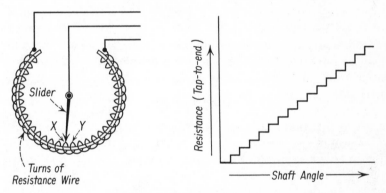

Fig. 2-5 Potentiometer Resolution

X to turn Y, the resistance between the slider and one end of the element will change by an amount equal to the resistance of one turn of wire. This is the minimum amount by which the resistance can be changed, and depends upon the size and resistivity of the wire and the length of each turn. Since the resistance changes by discrete amounts as the slider moves from turn to turn, the resistance changes in step fashion as the shaft is rotated. A plot of resistance versus shaft angle is shown in Fig. 2-5. The steps are exaggerated here for illustration. In an actual potentiometer, the number of steps would be greater and the amplitude of the individual steps would be smaller. The steps in Fig. 2-5 are drawn on the assumption that the width of the slider is equal to the spacing between turns; that is, the slider contacts the next turn at the instant it leaves the preceding turn. In practice, the slider is usually made wide enough to overlap several turns to provide better electrical contact, but the resistance still changes in step fashion.

The resolution of a potentiometer is expressed in terms of either *voltage resolution* or *angular resolution*. The voltage resolution expresses the ratio of the *voltage change per step* to the *total excitation voltage*. If, for example, an excitation potential of 5 v is applied across a 1,000-turn potentiometer, the amplitude of the voltage steps will be 0.005 v (again assuming that the slider contacts only one turn at a time). The voltage at the slider will therefore change in 5-mv steps as the slider moves from turn to turn. The voltage resolution is:

$$\frac{\text{voltage per step}}{\text{excitation voltage}} = \frac{0.005}{5} = 0.001 = 0.1\%$$

As indicated above, the resolution may be expressed as a percentage. Typical values of resolution for potentiometers designed for servomechanism applications are generally in the range of 0.1 to 0.002 percent.

The *angular resolution* of a potentiometer is numerically equal to the total winding angle divided by the total number of turns (assuming that the turns are equally spaced). Angular resolution therefore expresses the number of degrees of shaft rotation required to produce a one-step change of output voltage; that is, to move the slider from the center of one turn to the center of the next turn. If, for example, a 2,000-turn resistance element extends over an angle of 320 deg, the angular resolution is

$$\frac{320}{2,000} = 0.160 \text{ deg per turn}$$

Improved resolution can be achieved by using a greater number of turns of wire, but this approach is limited by such practical considerations as the over-all size of the potentiometer and the minimum size of resistance wire. The use of smaller diameter wire permits an increase in the number of turns without an increase in over-all dimensions, but smaller wire has less mechanical strength and wears more rapidly under slider friction.

Resolution is an important factor in servomechanism design because it determines the minimum value of error signal. It may happen, for example, that the voltage picked off by the slider of a follow-up potentiometer is 85 mv at one turn and 90 mv at the next turn. If the voltage at the slider of the command potentiometer is 87 mv, an exact balance cannot be achieved. The follow-up potentiometer will *hunt* back and forth between the two successive turns, seeking a value of voltage it cannot find. The magnitude of the turn-to-turn voltage steps can, of course, be reduced by decreasing the excitation voltage. This expedient however, results in a lower magnitude of error signal for a given difference of position of the command shaft and the follow-up shaft. More gain would then be required to amplify the error to a level sufficient to drive the motor or other error-correcting device.

The deposited film type of potentiometer is characterized by better resolution than the wire-wound variety. In this type, the resistance element consists of a thin layer of metal or carbon deposited on a base of insulating material. Excitation voltage is applied across the ends of the resistance film, and the slider moves over the surface of the film picking off a voltage determined by its position with respect to the ends of the film. In theory, the resolution of the film-type potentiometer is infinite because the slider moves over a continuous surface. In practice, however, the resolution is limited by the granularity of the film. Even so, the attainable resolution is much superior to that of the wire-wound potentiometer. A disadvantage of the deposited film potentiometer is that the resistance of the film changes with variations of temperature and humidity (to a greater extent than a wire-wound potentiometer exposed to the same conditions of environment).

2-4. LINEARITY

The linearity of a potentiometer is a measure of its ability to produce equal changes of slider voltage for equal changes of shaft position. In a perfectly linear potentiometer, for example, the slider voltage at a shaft angle of 80 deg will be exactly twice as great as the slider voltage at a shaft angle of 40 deg. This characteristic of the potentiometer can be expressed in another way: the voltage at the slider will change at a constant rate as the shaft is rotated at a constant rate.

Fig. 2-6 shows a graph of slider voltage plotted against shaft angle for a perfectly linear potentiometer. In a wire-wound potentiometer, the voltage at the slider changes in step fashion as

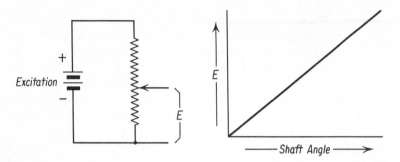

Fig. 2-6 Potentiometer Linearity

described previously. For the purpose of linearity considerations, however, the steps may be "averaged out" and the linearity represented by a smooth line as shown in Fig. 2-6. In practice, the limits of manufacturing precision establish the limits of linearity that can be realized. Deviations from perfect linearity are attributable to three principal causes: (1) the resistance wire may not be of constant diameter along its entire length, (2) the turns may not be spaced exactly equally, and (3) the turns may not be identical in size; that is, one turn may contain a greater length of wire than another turn. As a result of these limitations, the actual curve (voltage versus shaft angle) will deviate from the ideal straight line. This is illustrated in Fig. 2-7. The deviations from perfect linearity are exaggerated here for illustration.

The linearity of a potentiometer is usually specified in terms of the deviation from the ideal straight line at the point of maximum deviation. Assume, for example, that the voltage at the slider is 4.96 v when the ideal straight line calls for a value of 5 v,

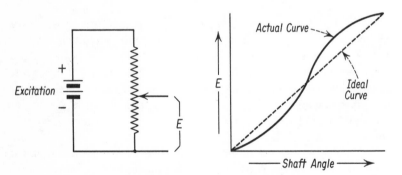

Fig. 2-7 Ideal and Actual Linearity

and that this is the point of maximum deviation from the ideal. If the excitation potential is 20 v, the linearity is:

$$\frac{5 - 4.96}{20} = \frac{0.04}{20} = 0.002 = 0.2\%$$

Deviations from perfect linearity are detrimental in many servomechanism applications because such deviation may result in the production of an error signal when the command shaft and the follow-up shaft are at the same angular positions. The slider of the command shaft, for example, may be at a potential of 5 v and the slider of the follow-up shaft may be at 4.96 v (with both shafts at the same angular position). Under these conditions, an error signal of 0.04 v will be produced and the motor will therefore rotate. The follow-up shaft will now move until its slider finds a potential of 5 v. The end result is that the command and follow-up shafts are not matched in position. Furthermore, it may happen that one potentiometer deviates "above" the straight line at the same shaft angle that the other potentiometer deviates "below" the straight line. This will result in an even greater mismatch of the command shaft and follow-up shaft.

The linearity of a potentiometer may often be improved by the use of a series *trimmer* resistor. Consider, for example, the potentiometer shown in Fig. 2-8(A). With an excitation potential of 10 v, point X (eight-tenths of the way up the resistance element) should be at a potential of 8 v. Suppose, however, that this point is at a potential of 8.1 v because of nonlinearity of the resistance ele-

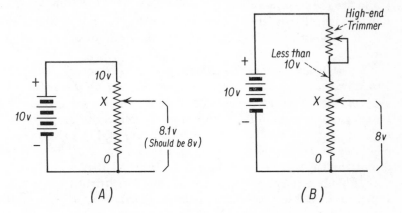

Fig. 2-8 Use of High-End Trimmer

ment. The voltage at point X can be reduced to its correct value (8 v instead of 8.1 v) by the use of a *high-end* trimmer as shown in Fig. 2-8(B). A portion of the excitation voltage is now dropped across the trimmer, leaving less than 10 v across the potentiometer. As a result, the voltage is lowered at all points along the resistance element of the potentiometer. The trimmer can be adjusted so that the potential at point X is exactly 8 v, bringing this point into coincidence with the ideal straight line.

It must not be assumed, however, that the use of a high-end trimmer will permit adjustment to *perfect* linearity. When the trimmer is adjusted to reduce the potential at point X to 8 v in the above example, the voltage at all other points along the resistance element will also be reduced. Consequently, points along the resistance element which were previously at correct potentials will now be too low (and points that were previously too low will now be still lower). Nevertheless, the use of a high-end trimmer is justified because the potentials below point X on the resistance element change by a smaller amount than the potential at and above point X. The previously correct potentials are therefore shifted only slightly when point X is brought to its correct value. Variation of the trimmer resistance produces the greatest voltage change at the high end of the potentiometer and correspondingly smaller changes toward the low end. The potential at the extreme low end of the potentiometer cannot be changed at all; no possible setting of the trimmer can reduce this point below zero potential. It is for this reason that the term *high-end* trimmer is used.

When a high-end trimmer is used, the high end of the potentiometer will be at a potential lower than the value of the excitation voltage; that is, the full excitation voltage is not available as output. In most applications, however, this is not an objectionable feature.

The use of a *low-end* trimmer is illustrated in Fig. 2-9. With 10 v of excitation, point Y (two-tenths of the way up the resistance element) should be at a potential of 2 v. Suppose, however, that this point is at a potential of 1.9 v because of nonlinearity of the resistance element. The potential at point Y can be raised to 2 v by means of a low-end trimmer as shown in Fig. 2-9(B). Because of the voltage drop across the trimmer, the potential is increased at all points along the resistance element of the potentiometer. The trimmer can be adjusted to make the potential at point Y exactly 2 v, bringing this point into coincidence with the ideal straight line. The presence of the trimmer resistance will, however, raise the potential at all other points along the resistance element of the potentiometer. Consequently, points that were previously at the correct potential will now be too high (and points that were previously too high will now be still higher). The use of a low-end trimmer is justified because the potentials above point Y on the resistance element change by a smaller amount than the potential at and below point Y. The previously correct potentials are therefore shifted only slightly when point Y is brought to its correct value. Variation of the trimmer resistance produces the greatest voltage change at the low end of the potentiometer, and correspondingly smaller changes toward the high end. The potential at the extreme high end of the poténtiometer cannot

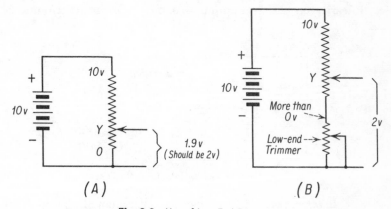

Fig. 2-9 Use of Low-End Trimmer

be changed at all; no possible setting of the low-end trimmer can raise this point above the potential of the excitation voltage. It is for this reason that the term *low-end* trimmer is used.

When a low-end trimmer is used, the potential at the slider cannot be reduced to zero as the slider is moved to the low end of the resistance element. In many applications, however, this is not an objectionable feature.

Since a high-end trimmer is more effective in shifting the potentials near the high end of the potentiometer, and a low-end trimmer produces larger changes near the low end of the potentiometer, both trimmers are often used. These trimmers can be adjusted for best *error split* so that the actual curve of the potentiometer (slider voltage versus shaft angle) does not deviate more in one direction than in the other with respect to the ideal straight line.

The trimmers can also be adjusted to make the actual curve coincide with the ideal curve at selected points or over a selected region.

In specifying percentage deviation from perfect linearity, it is important to indicate whether or not the specified percentage is based upon the use of trimmer resistors. Some manufacturers of precision potentiometers specify linearity percentage on the assumption that no trimmers are used, and others specify the linearity attainable *with* the use of trimmers. For clarification, the terms *terminal* linearity, *zero-based* linearity, and *independent* linearity are used. These terms are defined below.

Terminal linearity specifies the maximum deviation from perfect linearity of the potentiometer element itself (no trimmers).

Zero-based linearity specifies maximum deviation from perfect linearity on the assumption that only a high-end trimmer is used.

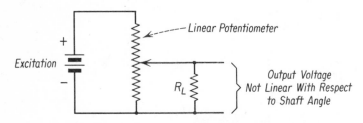

Fig. 2-10 Loading Resistor Introduces Nonlinearity

Independent linearity specifies maximum deviation from perfect linearity on the assumption that both high-end and low-end trimmers are used.

Another factor that contributes to nonlinearity, and that is not directly related to the potentiometer itself, is the so-called *loading error*. This is illustrated in Fig. 2-10. The presence of loading resistor R_L (which might, for example, represent the input impedance of the error amplifier) will result in nonlinear output even if the potentiometer itself is perfectly linear. The loading resistor is in parallel with the portion of the resistance element below the slider, and this parallel combination is in series with the portion of the resistance element above the slider. When the slider is moved, the resistance of the parallel combination changes at a different rate than the resistance above the slider. Slider voltage is therefore no longer linearly related to shaft angle. This loading error can be minimized by (1) making R_L large in value, (2) intentionally making the potentiometer nonlinear to compensate for the loading error (so that the combination of potentiometer and loading resistor will produce a linear output), and (3) providing fixed taps on the potentiometer across which external resistors can be connected to approximate the ideal straight-line characteristic.

2-5. CONFORMITY

Some applications require the use of nonlinear potentiometers. It may be required, for example, that the voltage at the slider vary according to the *sine* of the shaft angle. In such a potentiometer,

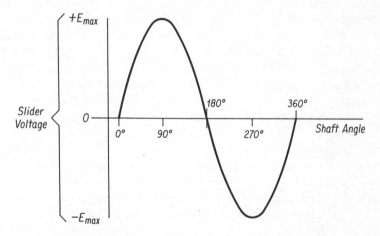

Fig. 2-11 Slider Voltage versus Shaft Angle for Sine Potentiometer

the slider voltage will reach half of its maximum value when the shaft is positioned at 30 deg (sin 30 deg = 0.5), and will reach maximum value at a shaft angle of 90 deg (sin 90 deg = 1). A graph of slider voltage versus shaft angle is shown in Fig. 2-11.

Since it is confusing (and meaningless) to refer to the "linearity" of a potentiometer that is intentionally made nonlinear, the term *conformity* is used in specifying how well the actual curve of a nonlinear potentiometer corresponds to the desired curve. Conformity is specified as the percentage of deviation from the desired curve (at the point of maximum deviation). This maximum deviation is expressed as a percentage of the applied excitation voltage. As in the case of linearity considerations, conformity may be expressed as *terminal* or *independent* depending on whether or not trimmer resistors are used.

Nonlinear potentiometers are sometimes designed to have a *function angle* smaller than the winding angle. A potentiometer may have a total winding angle of 320 deg, for example, but may be designed to produce the required output variations only between the limits of 20 and 300 deg. In such a case, the conformity is specified in terms of the maximum deviation expressed as a percentage of the excitation corresponding to the function angle (20 to 300 deg in the above example). Some manufacturers specify conformity as a peak-to-peak value to take into account the deviations both above and below the desired curve. *Constant fractional accuracy* is a term used by some manufacturers in specifying the accuracy of nonlinear potentiometers. This is similar to conformity except that the deviation is expressed as a percentage of the *correct* value at the point of maximum deviation, rather than as a percentage with respect to *total* excitation. Since the accuracy of a nonlinear potentiometer can be expressed in many ways, it is important to evaluate each manufacturer's specifications in terms of the appropriate definitions.

Many forms of nonlinearity are available in *standard* potentiometers, and others can be obtained on special order from the manufacturer. Some commonly available nonlinear functions are *sine* (slider voltage varies according to sine of shaft angle), *square-law* (slider voltage proportional to square of shaft angle), and *log* (slider voltage increases logarithmically as shaft angle is advanced).

A potentiometer can be made nonlinear by:

1. Winding the resistance wire unevenly so that spacing between turns varies over the length of the resistance element [Fig. 2-12(A)].

2. Changing to a different size wire at intervals along the resistance element, producing a number of "straight line" segments approximating the desired nonlinear curve [Fig. 2-12(B)].

3. Changing to a different type (material) of wire at intervals along the resistance element [Fig. 2-12(C)].

4. The use of contoured cards so that the length of wire per turn varies along the resistance element [Fig. 2-12(D)].

5. The use of stepped cards, producing a number of series-connected linear segments [Fig. 2-12(E)].

Two or more of the above techniques may be used in a

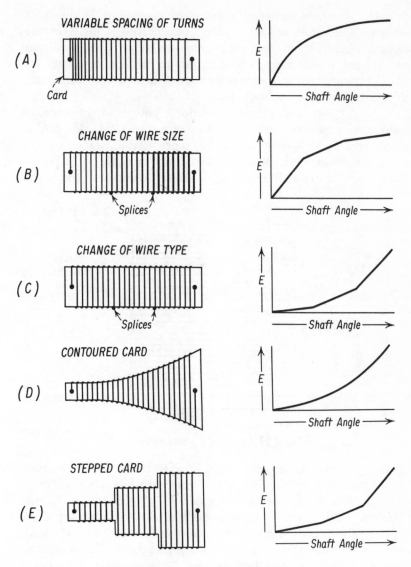

Fig. 2-12 Nonlinear Resistance Elements

single resistance element to achieve the desired type of nonlinearity. In the deposited film type of potentiometer, a film of nonuniform width (corresponding to a contoured card) produces the desired nonlinear function.

Certain types of nonlinearity can be achieved by connecting

an external resistor between the slider and one end of the resistance element. The values of the "loading" resistor and of the resistance element of the potentiometer determine the shape of the nonlinear curve. Some potentiometers have a number of fixed taps, and external resistors can be connected across these taps to approximate the desired form of nonlinearity.

Another useful form of nonlinear potentiometer is the so-called *square card* potentiometer. As shown in Fig. 2-13, the card is wound with evenly spaced turns of resistance wire. Excitation voltage is applied across the resistance element, and the shaft of the potentiometer moves two sliders along a circular path over the wires.

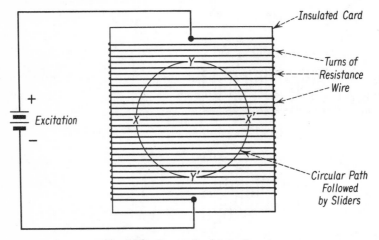

Fig. 2-13 Square-Card Potentiometer

When the shaft is at zero degrees, the two sliders are in the positions labeled X and X' in Fig. 2-13. At this time, the sliders are equidistant from the ends of the resistance element, and the potential difference between sliders is essentially zero. Output voltage (difference of potential of the two sliders) varies according to the sine of the shaft angle. If the shaft is moved to the 90-deg position, the sliders will be located at the positions labeled Y and Y'. At this time, the number of turns between sliders is maximum, and the voltage between sliders is therefore also maximum. As the shaft is rotated beyond 90 deg, the number of turns between sliders decreases again, so that the output voltage (like the sine of the angle) decreases between 90 and 180 deg. With the shaft at 180 deg, the two sliders are again at the same potential (sin 180 deg = 0). As the potentiometer shaft is rotated beyond

180 deg, the number of turns between sliders increases again. Now, however, the polarity of the slider-to-slider voltage is opposite as compared to the first 180 deg of shaft rotation. At a shaft angle of 270 deg, the output voltage is again maximum, and then decreases as the shaft is rotated toward 360 deg. A second pair of sliders, positioned 90 deg away from the first pair, can be used to produce an output proportional to the *cosine* of the shaft angle. Units of this type are referred to as sine-cosine potentiometers.

2-6. POTENTIOMETER CONSTRUCTION

A wire-wound resistor contains many turns of enamel-covered wire on an insulating card or on an enamel-covered metal rod (mandrel). This resistance element is mounted in the potentiometer case in such a position that the slider, controlled by the shaft, can move along a de-insulated path across the wires. Several factors dictate the choice of wire size. Small-diameter wire is preferable because a larger number of turns can be placed on an element of given physical dimensions, improving the resolution of the potentiometer. Larger wire however, offers the advantage of greater mechanical strength and higher power dissipation capabilities. Wire size is also a factor in lifetime considerations because small wire wears more rapidly under slider friction. The wire size selected for a particular application therefore represents a compromise of these conflicting factors. The wire resistivity (type of material) is selected in accordance with the total resistance required and the permissible temperature coefficient.

The metal contact of the slider must have satisfactory mechanical as well as electrical properties. It should have high electrical conductivity, low wear rate, and should not produce abrasive particles that will interfere with good electrical contact. The pressure of the contact upon the resistance element must be neither too great nor too small. Excessive pressure results in excessive wear and therefore reduces the useful lifetime of the potentiometer. Insufficient pressure results in poor electrical contact and high noise level. Potentiometer noise is produced by friction between the contact and the wires, by arcing at the contact, and by dust or other particles on the resistance element. Contact pressure is also an important factor for another reason. The greater the pressure, the greater the torque mechanical force) required to move the slider. Some applications require a low-torque potentiometer because of the small force available for moving the slider; for example, when the slider is positioned by an evacuated bellows responding to changes of air pressure.

Electrical continuity from the moving slider to an external terminal on the potentiometer case is established by means of a slip-ring assembly. A precious metal contact riding on a coin-silver slip-ring provides good electrical continuity and low noise level.

Each end of the resistance element is connected to a metal plate known as an *overtravel* (Fig. 2-14). The overtravel is fitted to

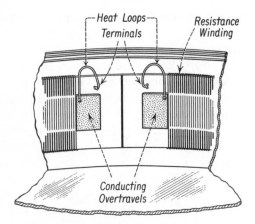

Fig. 2-14 Overtravels and Heat Loops
(Technology Instrument Corp.)

the insulating card so that the slider makes a smooth transition in moving from the last turn of wire onto the surface of the overtravel. Except in continuous rotation potentiometers, a mechanical stop is provided to limit the amount of slider travel. The stop is so positioned that, at the extremes of shaft angle, the slider comes to rest on the overtravel. The overtravels are approximately 10-deg wide. As shown in Fig. 2-14, heat loops connect the overtravels to the external terminals of the potentiometer. When leads are being soldered to these terminals, the loops minimize the amount of heat conducted to the resistance element.

The terms *overtravel* angle, *winding* angle, and *continuity* angle are illustrated in Fig. 2-15. Winding angle is measured from one electrical end point to the other; that is, the angle between the first and last turns of the resistance element. The continuity angle includes both the winding angle and the overtravel angles. The term *mechanical* angle is sometimes used and refers to the total angle through which the potentiometer shaft can be rotated. This, of course, is determined by the location of the mechanical stops.

The case of the potentiometer is made of metal, molded plastic, or a combination of the two. To maintain a dust-free, moisture-proof environment for the resistance element, the case is completely closed except for the small clearance between the shaft and the phosphor-bronze sleeve through which it passes. The shaft and sleeve should be close-fitting to maintain an effective seal against dirt and moisture. A grease seal may be used for this purpose. A tight-

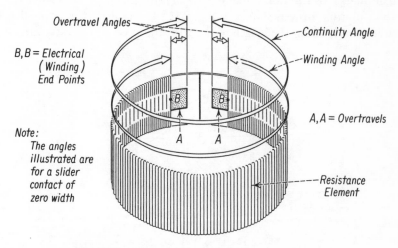

Fig. 2-15 Overtravel, Winding, and Continuity Angles
(Technology Instrument Corp.)

fitting sleeve, however, increases the torque requirements. For this reason, ball-bearing shaft supports are often used in low-torque potentiometers.

Potentiometers of special construction are available to meet the requirements of various applications. These special features of construction are described below.

Ganged Potentiometers

The shaft of the potentiometer passes completely through the case so that several of these potentiometers can be *ganged* and controlled simultaneously by a single shaft. Because of mechanical variations and limitations, it may happen that the slider in one potentiometer is several turns of wire "ahead" or "behind" the slider in another. The mounting arrangement is such that the individual potentiometers can be turned slightly on the common shaft. Adjustments can thus be made so that all sliders are on the "same" turn. This procedure is known as *phasing* the potentiometers.

Slide-Wire Potentiometer

In those applications which demand excellent resolution, either film or slide-wire potentiometers are used. The slide-wire potentiometer consists of a single turn of wire partially imbedded in an insulating form as shown in Fig. 2-16. As the shaft is turned, the slider moves along the length of the wire and produces stepless varia-

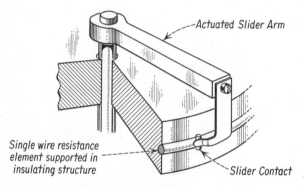

Actuated Slider Arm

Single wire resistance element supported in insulating structure

Slider Contact

Fig. 2-16 Slide-Wire Construction (Technology Instrument Corp.)

tions of output. One disadvantage of the slide-wire potentiometer is that the total resistance of the element is small. Errors may therefore be introduced because the resistance of the terminal leads as well as the resistance of the contact may be an appreciable percentage of the total resistance. The advantages of slide-wire construction are excellent resolution and linearity, low wear rate, and low torque requirement.

Linear-Travel Potentiometer

The distinguishing feature of the linear-travel potentiometer is that the shaft motion is translational (back and forth) rather than rotary. This type, which is also known as a *translatory* potentiometer, has a straight resistance element rather than a curved one. The element may be either wire-wound or deposited film, and both linear and nonlinear functions are available.

Multiturn Potentiometer

The multiturn potentiometer is distinguished from the single-turn variety by constructional features that permit more than 360 deg of shaft rotation (to move the slider from one end to the other of the resistance element). Three-turn and ten-turn (1080-deg and 3600-deg) models are commonly available. The resistance wire is wound on a rod-shaped mandrel, and the rod is then coiled to form

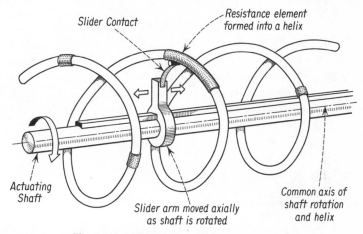

Slider Contact

Resistance element formed into a helix

Actuating Shaft

Slider arm moved axially as shaft is rotated

Common axis of shaft rotation and helix

Fig. 2-17 Multiturn Potentiometer Construction
(Technology Instrument Corp.)

a helix as shown in Fig. 2-17. Mechanical construction is such that the slider contact moves along the helix as the shaft is rotated. In some models, the resistance wire itself is wound in the form of a helix, resulting in a multiturn, slide-wire potentiometer.

The advantage of multiturn construction is that a lengthy resistance element can be contained in a relatively small case, permitting increased resolution without appreciable increase of physical size. Disadvantages of multiturn potentiometers are greater lag time (to bring the slider to the desired position), higher torque requirement, and higher inductive reactance to the excitation frequency.

The shaft of a multiturn potentiometer must be turned through several complete revolutions to move the slider along the

Fig. 2-18 Ten-Turn Direct-Reading Dial (Borg Equipment Division)

Fig. 2-19 Precision Potentiometer with Ball-Bearing Shaft Support (Computer Instruments Corp.)

full length of the resistance element. Multiturn indicator dials are therefore used to indicate shaft position. A dial of this type is shown in Fig. 2-18. This 10-turn dial features 3-digit, in-line presentation; the numerals are white on black or black on white for fast and accurate readability.

SUMMARY

Precision potentiometers are frequently employed in error-detector circuits. Two potentiometers connected as a bridge will produce an error voltage proportional to the angular difference of their shafts. If d-c excitation is applied to the bridge, the error signal will be a d-c potential whose polarity and magnitude will depend upon the direction and degree of unbalance of the bridge. If a-c excitation is employed, the error voltage will be an a-c signal whose phase and amplitude depend upon the direction and degree of unbalance of the bridge. In the servomechanism, the shaft of one of the potentiometers is mechanically coupled to the error-corrector motor. This *follow-up* potentiometer will therefore duplicate the shaft motion of the other (command) potentiometer.

The voltage at the slider of a wire-wound potentiometer changes in small steps as the slider is moved from wire to wire along the resistance element. The amplitude of these steps determines the *resolution* of the potentiometer. Film-type potentiometers have better resolution because the slider moves over a continuous film. This type however, is more affected by environmental factors such as temperature and humidity.

It is generally desirable that slider voltage change linearly with respect to shaft angle. Deviations from perfect linearity are unavoidable because of the limits of manufacturing precision. Trimmer resistors are often employed to improve the linearity of the potentiometer.

Some applications require the use of nonlinear potentiometers; for example, sine-cosine, square-law, and logarithmic. These nonlinear characteristics are achieved by changes of wire size in the resistance element, by changes of wire material, or by the use of stepped or contoured cards. The actual *slider-voltage* versus *shaft-angle* curve of the potentiometer deviates from the desired characteristic because of manufacturing tolerances. These deviations are expressed as the *conformity* rating of the potentiometer.

Special constructional features are required for some applications; for example, ganged, slide-wire, linear-travel, and multiturn potentiometers.

QUESTIONS

1. What is meant by the *resolution* of a potentiometer?
2. Explain the difference between voltage resolution and angular resolution.
3. For a given excitation voltage, what factors determine the amplitude of the resolution *steps* of a wire-wound potentiometer?
4. Compare the wire-wound and deposited-film potentiometers on the basis of resolution.
5. What is meant by the *linearity* of a potentiometer?
6. Explain the difference between terminal linearity and independent linearity.
7. What is *loading error*?
8. What is the difference between linearity and conformity?
9. Describe the construction of a contoured-card potentiometer, a stepped-card potentiometer, and a square-card potentiometer.
10. Explain the difference between *winding* angle and *continuity* angle.
11. What is a translatory potentiometer?
12. State one advantage and one disadvantage of a multiturn potentiometer as compared to a single-turn potentiometer.

Error Detectors:
Transducers

CHAPTER 3

3-1. INTRODUCTION

Industrially, servomechanism techniques are used for the measurement and control (or both) of such physical variables as temperature, pressure, liquid flow rate, and so forth. A generalized block diagram of a temperature recorder-controller is shown in Fig. 3-1. The voltage developed by the thermocouple (determined by the temperature to which it is exposed) is opposed by the voltage derived from a potentiometer connected across a *standard* voltage source. When the voltage at the slider is exactly equal to the voltage of the thermocouple, these two voltages exactly cancel and there is no input to the amplifier. Under these conditions, the motor does not rotate. Should the temperature change, however, the thermocouple voltage will no longer exactly balance the potentiometer voltage. The amplifier therefore receives an input equal to the difference of the two voltages. This input may be either positive or negative depending on whether the thermocouple voltage is larger or smaller than the potentiometer voltage; that is, depending on whether the temperature has increased or decreased. The motor, which is driven by the amplifier, will therefore rotate in one direction if the temperature has increased and in the opposite direction if the temperature has decreased. Since the motor is mechanically coupled (through a speed-reducing gear) to the shaft of the potentiometer, the slider position will change when the motor rotates. Such rotation continues until the slider finds a potential that balances the new value of thermocouple voltage. At this time the circuit is again balanced, there is no input to the amplifier, and the motor stops.

The shaft of the motor is also mechanically coupled to a pointer that moves over a calibrated scale. Since the motor rotates each time the temperature changes, and since the motor positions the pointer over the calibrated scale, a visual indication of temperature is provided. When a permanent record of temperature variations is desired, the motor may be coupled to a recording pen. This pen, riding on a threaded shaft, writes on a paper chart driven by a constant-speed motor. Changes of temperature therefore cause the pen to move in one direction or the other across the paper chart, producing a graph showing variations of temperature with respect to time. A system of pulleys is often used instead of the threaded shaft shown in Fig. 3-1, but the end result is the same.

If the instrument is to function as a controller as well as a recorder, the motor shaft may be coupled to a temperature regulating device—a valve in a fuel line, for example. A temperature increase will now cause the motor to rotate in a direction that reduces the fuel flow through the valve. A decrease of temperature will cause the motor to "open" the valve wider. In this manner, the fuel flow is regulated to keep the temperature constant.

The thermocouple and potentiometer in Fig. 3-1 function

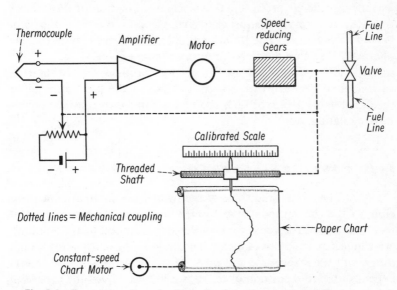

Fig. 3-1 Temperature Recorder-Controller Using Servomechanism Technique

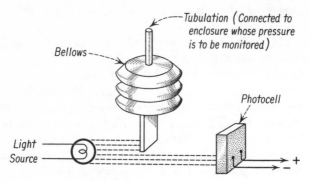

Fig. 3-2 Pressure-Sensing Technique

as an error detector, producing an error signal when the two voltages are unequal. For the measurement and control of variables other than temperature, some other type of transducer is substituted for the thermocouple. The pressure-sensing transducer shown in Fig. 3-2, for example, may be substituted for the temperature-sensing thermocouple. The tubulation of the bellows extends into the enclosure whose internal pressure is to be recorded or regulated. Should this internal pressure increase, the bellows will expand; a decrease of pressure will allow the bellows to contract (due to its "springiness" and the outside air pressure). The mechanical motion of the bellows is transmitted to an opaque vane that partially obstructs the light beam to a photocell. The illumination and the output voltage of the photocell therefore vary according to changes of pressure. As a result, the motor-driven pen in Fig. 3-1 will produce a trace showing variations of pressure with respect to time. If the pressure is to be regulated as well as recorded, the motor can be coupled to a pressure-regulating valve.

3-2. POSITION-SENSING TRANSDUCERS

The differential transformer, which is similar in basic principle to the conventional transformer, has a primary winding, two identical secondaries, and a movable core. The secondary windings are connected series-opposing so that the induced voltages buck each other, and the magnitude and phase of the secondary output (error) depends upon the position of the movable core. When the core (also known as an armature) is centered as shown in Fig. 3-3, there is equivalent coupling from primary to *both* secondaries. Since the two secondary voltages are of equal magnitude, they exactly cancel and no error output is produced. The primary and secondary polarities shown in Fig. 3-3 are for one half-cycle of excitation voltage. During the opposite half-cycle, the polarity of all three windings will be reversed so that the two secondaries still cancel each other.

In Fig. 3-3, it is assumed that the induced voltage in the secondary windings is 10 v. More important than the absolute values of these voltages however, is the *difference* of voltage of the two secondaries. This difference is the error output. In Fig. 3-4, the core is displaced in a upward direction from its center position. Secondary 1 is now linked by more flux lines than secondary 2. As a result of

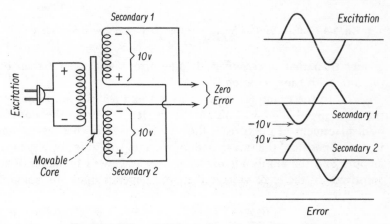

Fig. 3-3 Differential Transformer with Core Centered

the increased coupling to secondary 1 and the decreased coupling to secondary 2, the voltages induced in the two secondary windings are no longer equal. The difference, 0.2 v, therefore appears as an error voltage at the output terminals. The polarities of the induced voltages are shown for one half-cycle of excitation voltage. Since the voltage induced in secondary 1 is greater than that in secondary 2, the error signal polarity is the same as that of secondary 1. During the opposite half-cycle of excitation, polarity of all windings is reversed so that error polarity is still the same as that of secondary 1. As indicated by the waveforms in Fig. 3-4, the error signal is 180 deg *out of phase* with the excitation voltage.

If the core had been moved in a downward direction as shown in Fig. 3-5, the voltage induced in secondary 2 would be

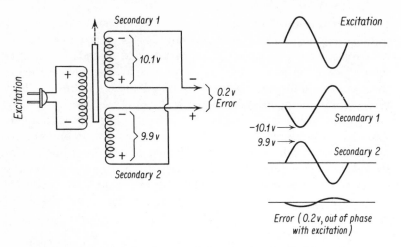

Fig. 3-4 Differential Transformer with Core Displaced toward Secondary I

greater than that of secondary 1. The error signal would then be *in phase* with the excitation.

In the examples shown Figs. 3-4 and 3-5, the amplitude of the error signal is 0.2 v. This amplitude depends upon the amount of displacement of the core. If the core is moved farther away from its center position, the two secondary voltages will differ by a greater amount and the amplitude of the error voltage will be larger. The amplitude of the error voltage therefore depends upon the amount

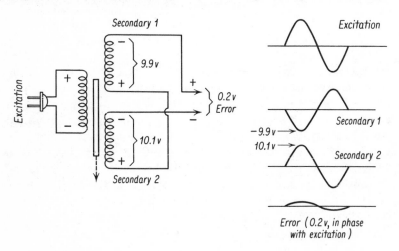

Fig. 3-5 Differential Transformer with Core Displaced toward Secondary 2

of movement of the core; the phase of the error signal depends upon the direction of movement away from the center position.

The differential transformer, also known as a *displacement* transformer, is available in several physical forms. The *E* transformer, so called because the core shape resembles the letter "E," is shown in Fig. 3-6(A). The primary is wound on the center leg of the *E* core, and the secondaries are on the outside legs. When the movable core is displaced in either direction indicated by the dotted arrows in Fig. 3-6(A), the secondary voltages no longer balance and an error signal is produced. Movement of the core may be translatory (in a direction parallel to the long axis of the core) or rotary as shown in Fig. 3-6(B). When rotary motion of the core is employed, only a limited amount of rotation is permissible. The amplitude of the error signal depends upon the amount of angular displacement of the core, and the phase of the error signal is determined by the direction of the angular displacement.

Another physical form of the differential transformer is shown in Fig. 3-7. In this *linear variable differential transformer* (LVDT), the primary and secondary windings form a hollow tube to contain the movable core. Motion of the core is translatory, and the transformer can be designed so that the amplitude of the error signal is linear with respect to core position. Several models of the linear differential transformer are shown in Fig. 3-8.

In theory, the error signal of a differential transformer is

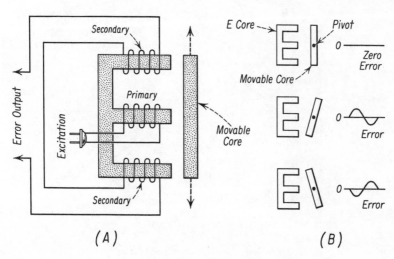

(A)   (B)

Fig. 3-6 E Transformer

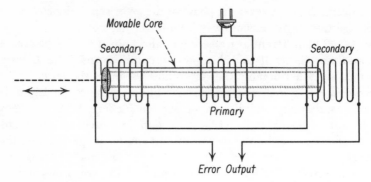

Fig. 3-7 Linear Variable Differential Transformer

zero when the core is exactly centered. In actuality however, some small amount of error voltage may remain because the two secondaries cannot be made absolutely identical. The core can be repositioned to compensate for differences of the two secondaries, but this may not reduce the error signal to zero. The off-center core produces phase shifts due to the difference of inductance of the two secondary windings. Because of this phase difference, the secondary voltages cannot exactly cancel even if they are equal in amplitude.

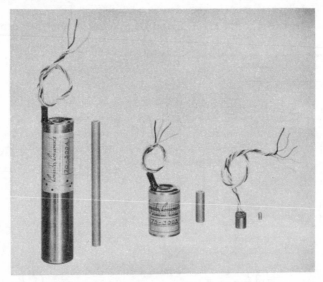

Fig. 3-8 Linear Motion Transducers
(International Resistance Co.)

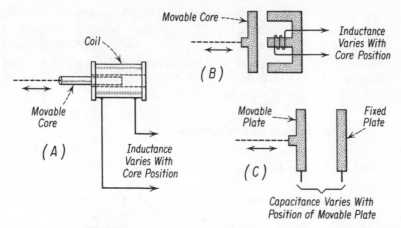

Fig. 3-9 Inductive and Capacitive Transducers

Careful design and construction can reduce this minimum *null* voltage to a negligible value.

Inductive and capacitive transducers are also useful for position-sensing applications. As shown in Fig. 3-9(A), the inductive transducer consists of a coil of wire and a movable iron core. The position of the core determines the value of inductance, and this inductance may be used in a bridge circuit. The output of the bridge will then be a measure of the mechanical position of the core. Alternatively, the inductance may be connected in the tank circuit of an oscillator. Under these conditions of operation, mechanical position is translated to a corresponding frequency of oscillation. *E*-type core construction is sometimes used and is illustrated in Fig. 3-9(B).

The capacitive transducer, Fig. 3-9(C), consists of two metal plates, one fixed in position and the other movable. Since the position of the movable element determines the spacing between the two plates, mechanical position is translated to a corresponding value of capacitance. This capacitance may be connected in a bridge circuit or used as a frequency-determining component of an oscillator.

3-3. TEMPERATURE TRANSDUCERS

Temperature is frequently one of the "controlled variables" in industrial processing and manufacturing operations, and temperature-sensing transducers are therefore widely used in many types of automatic control equipment. The characteristics desirable in a temperature transducer are (1) sensitivity to small variations of temperature, (2) high speed of response to temperature changes, and (3) the ability to withstand, without damage to itself, the range and changes of temperature to which it is exposed. Several types of temperature transducers are listed below.

Resistance Thermometer

The resistance thermometer consists of a coil of wire enclosed in a protective bulb. It is essentially a wire-wound resistor intentionally designed to have a large temperature coefficient. Nickel or platinum wire is used because of its relatively high resistance change with temperature. The resistance thermometer can be connected in a bridge circuit, and the output voltage of the bridge will be a function of temperature. A thin-wall protective bulb is used to permit rapid response to temperature changes.

Thermocouple

The thermocouple consists of two wires of dissimilar metals joined at one end. When this end (known as the hot junction) is heated, a voltage proportional to temperature is generated. The dissimilar metals used in the thermocouple are selected to produce a nearly linear voltage-versus-temperature characteristic, a relatively high voltage output per degree of temperature, and the ability to withstand a hot and sometimes corrosive environment. Copper-constantan thermocouples are generally used in the temperature range from —300 F to +600 F. Iron-constantan thermocouples are best suited to oxygen-deficient environments because the iron wire tends to oxidize. These are used in the range of 0 F to 1500 F. Chromel-alumel thermocouples are useful over a range of approximately 500 F to 2000 F.

The thermocouple is often enclosed in a protective bulb, and special fittings may be provided to facilitate mounting in a furnace wall, pipe, and so forth. Bulb mass and thickness are kept to a minimum to improve speed of response to temperature changes. Special extension wires are used to connect the thermocouple to the remainder of the equipment. These extension leads are frequently of the same dissimilar metals used in the thermocouple (to prevent undesired thermocouple action at the points of connection between the lead wire and the thermocouple element).

Thermistor

The thermistor is a temperature-sensitive resistor consisting of a mixture of various metallic oxides (manganese, cobalt, nickel, and so forth) processed and formed into the desired shape. Bead, disk, and rod shapes are the most common. The thermistor is generally more sensitive than the resistance thermometer; that is, its resistance changes by a greater amount for a given change of temperature. The thermistor is usually connected in a bridge circuit, and the output voltage of the bridge is therefore a function of temperature.

Phototubes

The phototube is used as a temperature transducer for higher temperature ranges, and is particularly useful for temperature measurement (and control) of molten metals. The molten metal emits radiation, both visible and infrared, in proportion to its temperature. This radiation, illuminating the cathode of the phototube, produces electron emission from the cathode. The plate current of the phototube is therefore a measure of the temperature of the molten metal.

3-4. PRESSURE TRANSDUCERS

Pressure, like temperature, is frequently one of the "controlled variables" in industrial processes. The bellows and Bourdon tube, used in conjunction with a position-sensing device, are widely used as pressure transducers.

The Bourdon tube is a hollow, thin-wall tube slightly flattened to produce an approximately elliptical cross section. The tube is sealed at one end and bent to a semicircular shape as shown in Fig. 3-10(A). The open end of the tube is connected into the system or enclosure whose pressure is to be monitored or controlled. This may be either air pressure (or other gases) or liquid pressure. The pressure inside the Bourdon tube tends to straighten it and therefore causes movement of the sealed end of the tube. Through mechanical linkages, this motion is transmitted to the core of a differential transformer, to the movable core of an inductive transducer,

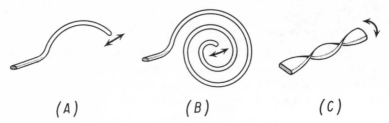

(A) (B) (C)

Fig. 3-10 Semicircular, Spiral, and Twisted Bourdon Tubes

to the movable plate of a capacitive transducer, or to the slider of a potentiometer. In this manner, pressure changes are converted to corresponding electrical changes.

The Bourdon tube is generally made of phosphor bronze, beryllium copper, or steel, and is useful for pressure measurements up to about 10,000 pounds per square inch.

Two variations of the basic Bourdon tube are the *spiral* and *twisted* types, illustrated in Figs. 3-10(B) and 3-10(C), respectively. The spiral type, as the name implies, consists of a long tube wound in the form of a spiral. This produces the effect of many semi-circular tubes connected end to end, and therefore amplifies the mechanical motion of the sealed end. Appropriate linkages transmit this motion to a position-sensing transducer.

The twisted type of Bourdon tube is twisted around its long axis as shown in Fig. 3-10(C). Pressure inside the tube tends to "untwist" it and therefore produces a rotary motion of the sealed end. This motion is coupled to a potentiometer shaft or to a differential transformer of the type shown in Fig. 3-6(B).

In the lower pressure ranges, the bellows is generally preferred to the Bourdon tube because of its greater mechanical force. Bellows are made of phosphor bronze, stainless steel, or brass, and expand or contract according to changes of pressure. Either the inside or the outside surface of the bellows may be exposed to the pressure to be monitored or controlled. In the former case, an increase of pressure will cause the bellows to expand; in the latter case, an increase of pressure will compress the bellows. In either case however, the mechanical motion resulting from a change of pressure is coupled to a position-sensing transducer (a differential transformer, for example).

The "springiness" of the bellows structure may be used as the balancing force against the applied pressure, but more often an internal spring is used for this purpose. An advantage of this spring-opposed bellows is that mechanical motion is more linearly related to pressure.

3-5. FLOW RATE, STRAIN, AND HUMIDITY

Flow-Rate Transducers

Industrial control systems frequently involve the measurement of flow rates of gas or liquid in a pipeline. In one of its popular forms, the flow-rate transducer contains a permanent magnet mounted in a special fitting connected in the pipeline. A turbine assembly attached to the magnet rotates at a rate determined by flow velocity, and the rotating magnet induces voltage in a nearby

Fig. 3-11 The Flow-Rate Transducer
(Fischer and Porter Co.)

pickup coil. The frequency of the induced voltage is therefore a function of flow rate. A gas-flow-rate transducer is shown in Fig. 3-11.

Another type of flow-rate transducer employs the hot-wire anemometer principle. This depends upon the cooling effect of the stream on an electrically heated wire: the greater the stream velocity, the greater the cooling effect. Heating current for the wire is supplied by a constant-current source so that wire temperature depends upon stream velocity. The resistance of the wire, which varies with temperature, is therefore a measure of flow rate. In a variation of this technique, external circuitry varies the wire current to keep the temperature constant. The value of this current is therefore proportional to flow velocity.

Strain Gauge

Strain-gauge techniques are used for measuring the minute dimensional changes which occur when a structure is subjected to an applied force. Strain measurements in aircraft and missile structures, for example, permit the designer to locate "weak spots" and to achieve a satisfactory compromise of the conflicting goals of maximum strength and minimum weight. Bridge and highway engineers use similar methods. The strain gauge can also be used as a pressure transducer because pressure inside a pipe or other enclosure will produce dimensional changes.

Basically, the strain gauge consists of a length of resistance wire bonded (cemented) to the structure to be studied. Structural strains cause the wire to stretch, reducing its diameter and therefore increasing its resistance. This resistance is connected in a bridge circuit so that bridge output voltage is a function of strain. For pressure sensing applications, the strain gauge is often mounted in a pressure capsule. One end of the capsule is a flexible diaphragm and is exposed to the gas or liquid whose pressure is to be monitored. Motion of the diaphragm, resulting from pressure changes, is coupled to the strain-gauge wire and produces a corresponding change of resistance.

Humidity Transducer

In one of its commonest forms, the humidity transducer consists of a moisture-absorbent chemical deposited on an insulating base. A coating of lithium chloride, for example, may be deposited on a strip of glass or plastic. Terminals are provided for establishing electrical connection to the coating. When the chemical coating absorbs moisture from the surrounding air, its electrical resistance decreases. As in the case of other "resistive" transducers, the humidity transducer may be connected in a bridge circuit. Variations of humidity will then produce variations of bridge output voltage.

SUMMARY

Transducers are employed for sensing the values of non-electrical quantities such as temperature, pressure, flow rate, and so forth. The transducer converts the nonelectrical quantity to a corresponding value of voltage, current, resistance, capacitance, or inductance. A differential transformer, for example, is a transducer for sensing mechanical position and for producing output voltage representative of this position. This type of transformer contains two secondary windings connected series opposing. When the movable core of the transformer is centered, the secondary voltages are equal and cancel each other. When the core is moved away from its center position, unequal voltages are induced in the secondaries. The voltage *difference* is the output (error) voltage and represents the position of the core. The *E* transformer and the LVDT are special forms of the differential transformer.

Thermistors and resistance thermometers are temperature transducers of the "resistive" type. In each case, the ohmic value of the transducer varies with temperature. The resistance thermometer is essentially a wire-wound resistor (nickel or platinum), and the thermistor is made of oxides of manganese, cobalt, and nickel.

Thermocouples are temperature transducers constructed of dissimilar metals. Phototubes responding to the radiation emitted from heated substances function as temperature-to-current transducers.

Bellows and Bourdon tubes are pressure-responsive components which produce mechanical motion in response to pressure changes. This motion can be transmitted to the slider of a potentiometer or to the movable core of a differential transformer to achieve pressure-to-voltage conversion.

Flow rate of liquid or gas can be monitored by a turbine-driven magnet in the pipeline or duct. Output voltage proportional to flow rate appears in a pickup coil mounted near the rotating magnet.

The strain gauge and the humidity sensor are "resistive" transducers. The former responds to dimensional changes and the latter to moisture absorbed from its surroundings.

QUESTIONS

1. Describe the changes that occur in the output of a differential transformer as the core is moved from one extreme to the other.
2. Describe the construction of the *E* transformer and the LVDT.
3. Name two types of temperature-sensing transducers.
4. Name two types of pressure-sensing transducers.

5. Name two types of transducers which produce output in the form of mechanical motion.

6. Name two types of transducers which produce output in the form of resistance variation.

7. Describe the construction and operation of a twisted Bourdon tube.

8. What is the advantage ot using a spring to oppose the motion of a bellows?

Error Detectors: Synchros

4-1. INTRODUCTION

Although it is generally larger than most other types of error detectors, the synchro is often used as an error detector component because of its high sensitivity and practically infinite resolution. The synchro, often referred to as a *selsyn* (trade name of General Electric Co.), combines the principle of the electric motor with the principle of the transformer. Like a motor, the synchro has stationary windings and shaft-mounted rotor windings; as in a transformer, one winding functions as primary and the other as secondary. Either the rotor or the stator windings may be used as the primary, depending upon the type of synchro and its intended application.

In the *synchro transmitter*, the rotor functions as a primary and the stator windings are secondaries. Since the angle of the rotor with respect to the stator windings can be changed by turning the shaft, the primary-to-secondary coupling can be varied. The induced secondary voltage therefore depends upon the angle of the rotor shaft. For this reason, the synchro transmitter can be regarded as a *position-to-voltage* transducer.

In the *synchro receiver*, the stator windings generate a magnetic field whose direction and strength are determined by the applied voltages. The rotor then turns until it has aligned itself with the magnetic field of the stator. The shaft angle assumed by the rotor therefore depends upon the voltage applied to the stator windings. For this reason, the synchro receiver can be regarded as a *voltage-to-position* transducer.

4-2. THE SYNCHRO TRANSMITTER

As indicated in Fig. 4-1, the synchro transmitter has a rotor winding and three Y-connected stator windings. The three stator windings are positioned 120 deg apart, and one end of each winding is connected to a common point. This common terminal is not accessible from the outside, but the free ends of the stator windings are brought out to external terminals on the case of the synchro. These terminals are identified as S_1, S_2, and S_3. The rotor leads are also brought out to external terminals which are identified as R_1 and R_2.

As shown in Fig. 4-1, the rotor winding is connected to the source of excitation voltage and therefore functions as a transformer primary. Since the stator windings function as secondaries, and since the voltage induced in a secondary depends upon the angle at which the magnetic lines of force cut across the turns, the voltage induced in any of the three secondaries is determined by the physical position of the rotor. Fig. 4-2 illustrates the relationship between the position of the rotor and the amount of voltage induced in stator winding S_2. For reference purposes, the zero-degree position of the rotor is defined as the position in which the rotor is aligned with stator coil S_2. In this position, the coupling between primary (rotor) and secondary S_2 will be maximum and induced voltage will also be maximum. This condition is illustrated in Fig. 4-2(A).

If the rotor is now moved away from the zero-degree position, the coupling to S_2 will decrease and the voltage induced in S_2

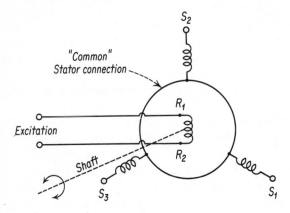

Fig. 4-1 The Synchro Transmitter

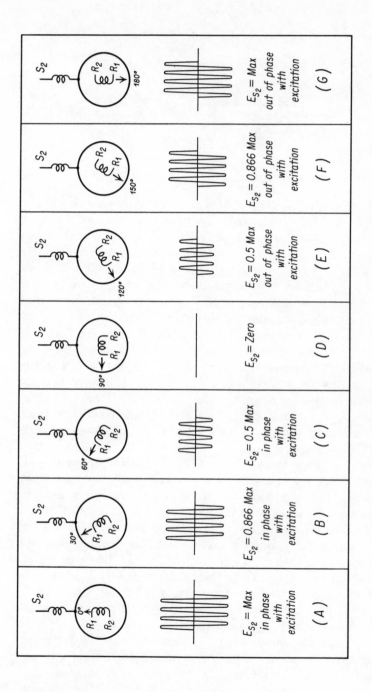

Fig. 4-2 Relationship between Induced Voltage in S_2 and Position of Shaft

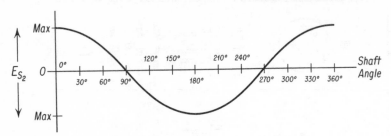

Fig. 4-3 Voltage Induced in S_2 versus Shaft Angle

will likewise decrease. The induced voltage varies according to the cosine of the shaft angle. With the rotor positioned at 30 deg as shown in Fig. 4-2(B), the voltage induced in S_2 will be only about 87 percent of the voltage induced when the rotor was at zero degrees (cos 30 deg = 0.866). At a rotor position of 60 deg, the voltage induced in S_2 will be only 50 percent of the voltage induced at a shaft angle of zero degrees (cos 60 deg = 0.5). When the rotor is positioned at 90 deg, the induced voltage will be zero (cos 90 deg = 0). Beyond 90 deg, the rotor begins to align itself with S_2 again and the induced voltage increases. Now, however, the rotor has passed through the horizontal position so that the R_2 end is "top" and the R_1 end is "bottom." The voltage induced in S_2 is therefore of opposite phase as compared to the induced voltage at rotor angles less than 90 deg. At a shaft angle of 180 deg, the rotor is again aligned with S_2 and the induced voltage is again maximum (but of opposite phase as compared to the induced voltage when the shaft was at zero degrees). As the shaft is advanced from 180 to 270 deg, the induced voltage decreases again and then, from 270 to 360 deg the induced voltage increases. A graph of induced voltage versus shaft angle is shown in Fig. 4-3.

The voltage induced in S_2 does not adequately identify the rotor position. An induced voltage of zero, for example, does not indicate whether the shaft angle is 90 or 270 deg. Likewise, the induced voltage is the same at a shaft angle of 30 deg as it is at an angle of 330 deg; it is the same at 60 deg as it is at 300 deg; and so forth. A single stator winding is therefore incapable of providing an unambiguous indication of shaft position.

Since the synchro has three stator windings 120 deg apart, the primary-to-secondary coupling to one stator increases as the coupling to another stator decreases. As the rotor is advanced from 0 to 60 deg, for example, the coupling to S_2 decreases but the cou-

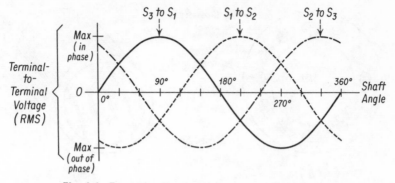

Fig. 4-4 Terminal-to-Terminal Voltage versus Shaft Angle

pling to S_1 increases. The induced voltage in S_1 therefore increases while the voltage in S_2 is decreased. Because the common terminal of the stator windings is not accessible from the outside of the synchro housing, it is common practice to specify the stator output voltages in terms of terminal-to-terminal voltage; that is, S_1 to S_2, S_1 to S_3, and S_2 to S_3. The magnitudes of these three terminal-to-terminal voltages are plotted as a function of shaft angle in Fig. 4-4. It is important to note that these three curves do not represent the waveforms of the induced voltages plotted against time, but rather represent the variations of the rms values of the induced voltages as the shaft angle is changed. The portions of the three curves above the horizontal axis indicate induced voltage *in phase* with the excitation, and the portions below the horizontal axis represent induced voltage 180 deg *out of phase* with respect to the excitation. As an example, at a rotor angle of 60 deg, the voltage between terminals S_2 and S_3 is zero because the voltages in these two windings cancel each other in the series connection. The voltage between terminals S_1 and S_3 is near maximum and in phase with the excitation. The voltage between terminals S_1 and S_2 is near maximum but is 180 deg out of phase with the excitation voltage. As indicated, the three terminal-to-terminal voltages identify the shaft angle; that is, for no two positions of the shaft will these voltages be identical.

Synchro Construction

The stator of the synchro transmitter is a laminated iron structure with the windings placed in slots as shown in the cross-sectional view in Fig. 4-5(A). The stator coils are divided electrically

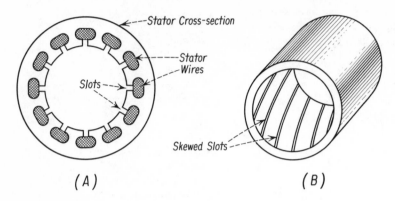

Fig. 4-5 Stator Construction

into three groups which are spaced 120 deg apart. When the stator laminations are stacked, each lamination is turned slightly with respect to the preceding lamination so that the slots do not exactly line up with those of the preceding lamination. The slot structure is therefore *skewed*; that is, the slots are not parallel to the shaft of the rotor. This skew, illustrated in Fig. 4-5(B), distributes the magnetic field in such a way that the rotor does not tend to *lock* in preferred positions with respect to the slots.

The rotor winding is placed on a laminated structure shaped as shown in the cross-sectional view in Fig. 4-6. The ends of the rotor laminations are curved to produce a small air gap between rotor and stator structures. The rotor shaft is ball-bearing supported to reduce friction losses. A pair of slip rings on an insulated portion of the shaft and a pair of brushes maintain electrical contact between the rotor winding and the external terminals.

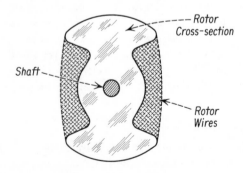

Fig. 4-6 Rotor Construction

4-3. *THE SYNCHRO RECEIVER*

The synchro transmitter is a position-to-voltage transducer in which the mechanical position of the rotor is represented by a set of terminal-to-terminal stator voltages. By contrast, the synchro receiver is a voltage-to-position transducer. For a given set of voltages applied to the stator windings, the synchro receiver will position its rotor to a corresponding angle. An example is shown in Fig. 4-7. Voltages from an external source are applied to the stator terminals. The stator windings therefore generate a magnetic field whose strength and direction are determined by the applied terminal-to-terminal voltages. The rotor, connected to an excitation source, also generates a magnetic field. For the magnetic polarities shown in Fig. 4-7, the rotor will turn in a counterclockwise direction. These magnetic polarities are shown for one half-cycle of applied voltage. During the opposite half-cycle, all magnetic polarities are reversed and the rotor motion is still in the counterclockwise direction. The forces of magnetic attraction and repulsion therefore produce a motor-like action with the stator functioning as a field winding and the rotor as an armature.

In addition to the motor action described above, transformer action also takes place. The rotor, functioning as a primary winding, induces voltage in the stator windings. These induced voltages depend upon the angular position of the rotor with respect to the stators. The rotor turns until it reaches the position in which the voltages it induces in the stator windings exactly cancel the

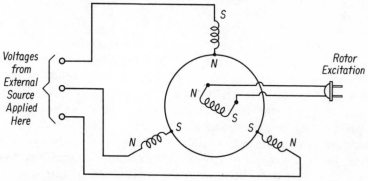

Fig. 4-7 Magnetic Polarities Cause Counterclockwise Rotation of Rotor

Excitation

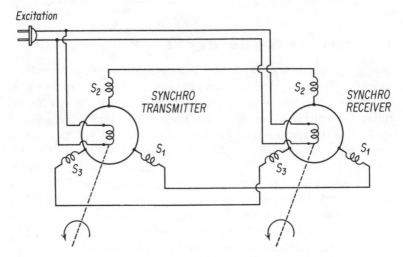

Fig. 4-8 Receiver Shaft Follows Motion of Transmitter Shaft

externally applied stator voltages. At this time, the net voltage in the stator windings is zero. Since stator current is also zero, the stator no longer generates a magnetic field and the rotor stops in this position. In this manner, the rotor assumes a position determined by the externally applied stator voltages. The curves shown in Fig. 4-4 for the synchro transmitter apply also for the synchro receiver. The receiver rotor will stop at an angle of 150 deg, for example, when the externally applied stator voltages are as follows:

S_3 to S_1: half of maximum and in phase with rotor excitation
S_1 to S_2: half of maximum and in phase with rotor excitation
S_2 to S_3: maximum and 180 deg out of phase with rotor excitation

The externally applied stator voltages referred to in the above explanation are usually supplied by a synchro transmitter. The transmitter and receiver are therefore used in combination as shown in Fig. 4-8. The transmitter rotor, acting as a primary, induces voltage in the transmitter stators. These stator voltages are applied to the stator windings in the receiver. The receiver stator therefore generates a magnetic field, causing the receiver rotor to turn. The receiver rotor turns until it reaches an angular position equivalent to that of the rotor in the transmitter. At this time, the induced voltages in the receiver stators exactly cancel the induced voltages in the transmitter stators. Stator currents are now zero and the receiver rotor stops turning. If the transmitter rotor is now turned to a different angular position, the receiver rotor will turn until it reaches a corresponding position. In this manner, any motion of the transmitter shaft is duplicated by the receiver shaft. The transmitter-receiver combination therefore synchronizes the motion of two shafts without requiring mechanical coupling. Such combinations are useful for remote positioning applications (if the mechanical load on the receiver is not too great) and for remote indication applications (in which a pointer attached to the receiver shaft indicates the angular position of the remotely located transmitter shaft).

The physical structure of the synchro receiver is similar to that of the transmitter except that the receiver is provided with a mechanical damper. Without damping, the receiver rotor would move too rapidly. It would rotate beyond the correct position, reverse its direction, overshoot going the other way, reverse its direction, overshoot going the other way, reverse its direction again, overshoot again, and so on. This "oscillation" would be particularly likely to happen when power is first applied to the system and the receiver attempts to align itself with the transmitter. Another possibility is that the momentum of the rotor may carry it beyond the correct position and through a complete revolution. Under these conditions, the rotor will "spin" continuously in true motor fashion.

4-4. THE SYNCHRO CONTROL TRANSFORMER

Because it can provide only a limited amount of torque, the synchro receiver is used only for positioning light loads (the pointer of an indicator, for example). Heavy loads will not only exceed the torque capabilities of the receiver but will also reduce the accuracy of the system. For these reasons, the *synchro control transformer* is often used instead of the synchro receiver in servomechanism applications. The control transformer produces an error signal whose magnitude and phase represent the amount and direction of error of an output shaft as compared to an input (command) shaft. The arrangement of components is shown in Fig. 4-9. The command shaft (rotor of the synchro transmitter) is adjusted to represent the desired position of the load (an antenna, for example). The load is mechanically coupled to the rotor of the control transformer. An error of load position will therefore produce an error in the position of the

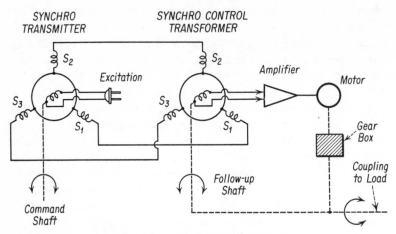

Fig. 4-9 Servomechanism Employing Synchros

rotor of the control transformer; that is, the shaft of the control transformer will not correspond in position to the command shaft. Under these conditions, the control transformer produces an error signal. The error voltage is amplified and used to control a motor which positions the load. As the load approaches the desired position, the rotor of the control transformer approaches a position corresponding to that of the command shaft. The error voltage therefore decreases, reaching zero when the angle of the control transformer shaft is equivalent to that of the command shaft. The load is now in the desired position and the motor stops.

Like the stator of a transmitter or receiver, the stator of the synchro control transformer consists of three Y-connected windings spaced at 120-deg intervals. These stator windings are energized by voltages from an external source (synchro transmitter), and the resulting current flow generates a composite magnetic field. The direction of this field depends upon the magnitude and phase of the applied terminal-to-terminal voltages. The direction of the composite magnetic field established in the control transformer therefore depends upon the angular position of the transmitter rotor. In Fig. 4-10(A), the transmitter rotor (and its magnetic field) are positioned at zero degrees. At this time, the composite magnetic field in the control transformer will be in the same direction (0 deg). In Fig. 4-10(B), the transmitter rotor has been advanced to 30 deg. With the rotor (primary) at this angle, the voltages induced in the transmitter stators are now different than they were previously. This new set of terminal-to-terminal voltages, applied to the stators of the control transformer, generates a magnetic field in the 30-deg direction. In this manner, the direction of the field in the control transformer can be changed by varying the position of the transmitter rotor.

Since the voltage induced in the rotor of the control transformer depends upon the angle at which its turns are cut by the magnetic field of the stators, the induced voltage in the rotor is determined by (1) the angular position of the transformer rotor and (2) the angular direction of the magnetic field of the stators. The angular direction of the magnetic field however, depends upon the shaft angle of the transmitter. The end result is that the magnitude and phase of the voltage induced in the rotor of the control transformer depend upon the angular *difference* of the two shafts (transmitter and control transformer).

Electrical zero (0 deg) of the control transformer is defined as the shaft angle at which the rotor is perpendicular to stator S_2 as shown in Fig. 4-11. Here, both shafts are positioned at zero degrees. The composite stator field in the transformer is therefore in

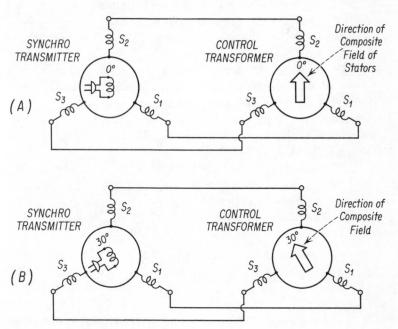

Fig. 4-10 Transmitter Controls Direction of Stator Field in Control Transformer

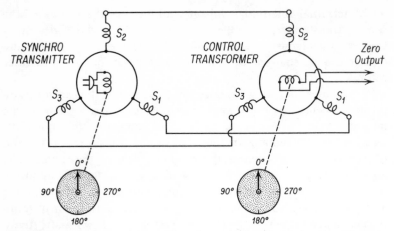

Fig. 4-11 Transmitter and Control Transformer Shafts Positioned at Zero Degrees

the zero-degree direction. Since the lines of force of this field are parallel to the rotor windings, no voltage is induced in the rotor. If either shaft in Fig. 4-11 is now moved, the stator field of the control transformer will cut *across* the rotor windings. Voltage will now be induced in the rotor according to the angle at which its turns are cut by the magnetic field. If the angular difference of the two shafts is increased to 90 deg, the magnetic field of the transformer stators will cut across the turns of the rotor at right angles. The voltage induced in the rotor will therefore be maximum. Note that it is the *difference* of shaft angles rather than the absolute values of these angles that determines the amount of voltage induced in the transformer rotor. The induced voltage will be maximum whether the two shafts are positioned at 0 and 90 deg, 10 and 100 deg, 200 and 290 deg, and so forth.

Numerically, the voltage induced in the transformer rotor is equal to the sine of the *difference* angle multiplied by the maximum value of induced voltage. If the maximum induced voltage (when the difference angle is 90 deg) is 55 v rms, for example, the induced voltage at an angular difference of 30 deg will be:

$$E_{\text{induced}} = E_{\text{max}} \ (\sin 30 \text{ deg})$$
$$= 55 \ (0.5)$$
$$= 27.5 \text{ v rms}$$

Fig. 4-12 shows a graph of induced voltage plotted against difference angle.

The voltage induced in the rotor of the control transformer may be either *in phase* or 180 deg *out of phase* with the excitation applied to the transmitter rotor. This depends upon whether the transformer shaft angle leads or lags the transmitter shaft. This is illustrated in Fig. 4-13. Shaft angle is considered to be "increasing" when the shaft is rotated counterclockwise (viewed from the shaft end of the synchro). The transformer shaft therefore *leads* the transmitter shaft by 60 deg in Fig. 4-13(A). The induced voltage in the transformer rotor is therefore about 87 percent of the maximum rms value (sine 60 deg = 0.866) and is *in phase* with transmitter rotor excitation. In Fig. 4-13(B), the transformer shaft *lags* the transmitter shaft by 60 deg. Induced voltage in the transformer rotor is therefore 0.866 of maximum but is 180 deg *out of phase* with transmitter rotor excitation.

When the control transformer is used as a component of a servomechanism, as in Fig. 4-9, the angular difference between command shaft and follow-up shaft is kept to small values by the corrective action of the system. For small values of angular difference, the error voltage is very nearly linear with respect to this difference as shown in Fig. 4-12.

When a synchro transmitter is connected to a control transformer as in Fig. 4-11, there are *two* positions of the transformer shaft that will result in zero induced voltage in the transformer rotor. If the transmitter and the transformer shafts are both at 10 deg, for

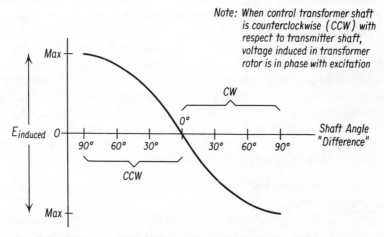

Fig. 4-12   Voltage Induced in Rotor of Control Transformer Plotted against Angular Difference of Shafts

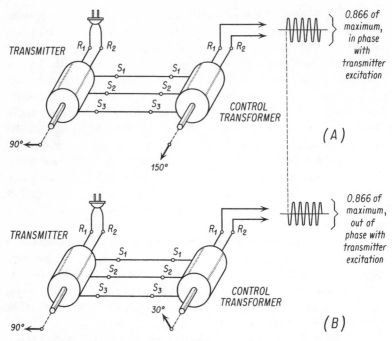

Fig. 4-13 Control Transformer Output May Be In Phase or 180 Deg
Out of Phase with Transmitter Excitation

example, the transformer rotor windings are parallel to the magnetic
field and induced voltage is zero. Now assume that the transmitter
shaft is left in the 10-deg position and that the transformer shaft is
rotated 180 deg to the 190-deg position. The rotor windings of the
transformer are again parallel to the magnetic field and induced
voltage is again zero. The control transformer therefore has two
zero-output positions, 180 deg apart. When the control transformer
is connected as a component of a servomechanism as in Fig. 4-9, the
correct zero-output position must be selected (otherwise the system
will tend to increase rather than decrease the amount of error). One
method of determining which of the two zero-output positions of
the rotor is the correct one is as follows:

1. Set the control transformer shaft to one of the zero-
output positions.

2. Rotate the transformer shaft slightly counterclockwise.

3. If the voltage now induced in the transformer rotor is
in phase with the excitation applied to the transmitter rotor, the

position selected in step 1 above is correct. (If the incorrect zero-output position had been selected in step 1, counterclockwise movement of the shaft would have produced an error signal 180 deg out of phase with transmitter excitation.)

4-5. THE SYNCHRO DIFFERENTIAL

As described in the preceding section, a control transformer produces an output (error) voltage which depends upon the angular difference of two shafts. Assume now that this error signal is applied to a synchro receiver as shown in Fig. 4-14. The transmitter shaft is shown at an angle of 100 deg, and the transformer shaft is at 70 deg. The error signal produced by the control transformer is therefore an electrical representation of a 30-deg difference angle. This electrical input to the receiver produces a magnetic field that positions the receiver rotor at an angle of 30 deg. The receiver shaft therefore assumes an angular position equal to the angular difference of the other two shafts. Such a relationship is desirable in certain servomechanism and computer applications.

Fig. 4-14 illustrates a principle, but in actual practice the control transformer could not be connected to the receiver as shown. The two-terminal rotor of the transformer cannot supply a set of three terminal-to-terminal voltages for the stators of the receiver. This difficulty can be overcome by modifying the rotor of the control transformer. The rotor can be made with three windings, Y-connected and spaced at 120-deg intervals. With this type of rotor, the unit is known as a *synchro differential* rather than a control transformer. Fig. 4-15 shows the practical arrangement needed to imple-

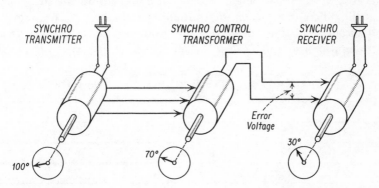

Fig. 4-14 Receiver Angle Equals Difference Angle of Other Two Shafts

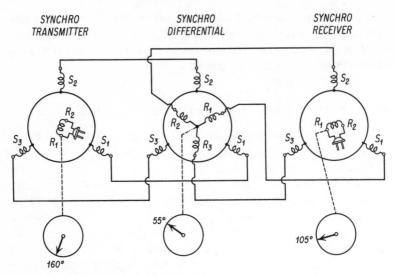

Fig. 4-15 Practical Arrangement for Principle Illustrated in Fig. 4-14

ment the principle illustrated in Fig. 4-14. The voltages induced in the three rotor windings of the synchro differential constitute an electrical representation of the difference angle of the two input shafts (transmitter and differential). These position-equivalent voltages are applied to the stators of the receiver, causing the receiver shaft to position itself accordingly.

The resulting position of the receiver shaft for various positions of the transmitter and differential shafts are tabulated in Fig. 4-16. All angles are specified as counterclockwise with respect to electrical zero (0 deg). In each case, the shaft angle of the receiver is equal to the shaft angle of the transmitter *minus* the shaft angle of the differential. When the transmitter shaft is at 270 deg and the differential shaft is at 260 deg, for example, the receiver shaft assumes a position of 270 deg — 260 deg = 10 deg. When the trans-

TRANSMITTER SHAFT	DIFFERENTIAL SHAFT	RECEIVER SHAFT
270°	260°	10°
195°	195°	0°
120°	125°	355°
45°	95°	310°

Fig. 4-16 Transmitter, Differential, and Receiver Shaft Positions

mitter and differential shafts are at 45 and 95 deg, respectively, the receiver shaft will be at an angle of 45 deg — 95 deg = —50 deg. This negative angle indicates a clockwise displacement of 50 deg from the 0-deg reference and is therefore equivalent to 310 deg.

It may be desirable in some applications to have the receiver shaft position itself to the *sum* angle rather than to the difference angle of the other two shafts. This can be accomplished by reversing connections as shown in Fig. 4-17. Such reversal has the effect of rotating the magnetic fields in the synchros, positioning the rotor of the receiver to the *sum* position.

The synchro differential is sometimes used in conjunction with two transmitters as shown in Fig. 4-18. One transmitter supplies the terminal-to-terminal voltages for the stators of the differential; the other transmitter supplies the terminal-to-terminal voltages for the rotors of the differential. In the differential, the composite field of the stators interacts with the composite field of the rotors. The forces of magnetic attraction and repulsion move the rotor to an angular position representing the difference angle of the two transmitter shafts. The differential may be made to indicate the *sum* angle rather than the difference angle by interchanging its R_1 and R_3 connections.

When a synchro differential is used to control a receiver, as in Fig. 4-15, it is referred to as a *synchro differential transmitter*. When the differential itself functions as the controlled unit (receiver), as in Fig. 4-18, it is referred to as a *synchro differential receiver*. Physically, the differential transmitter and the differential receiver are similar except that the receiver has an oscillation damper

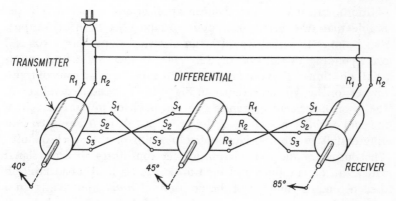

Fig. 4-17 Connections for Addition of Input Angles

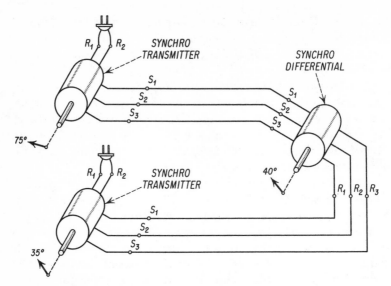

Fig. 4-18 Synchro Differential Controlled by Two Transmitters

to minimize hunting. In both types, slip rings and brushes establish electrical contact between the rotor windings and the external terminals R_1, R_2, and R_3. Electrical zero (0 deg) of the differential is defined as the shaft position which aligns rotor R_1 with stator S_1, rotor R_2 with stator S_2, and R_3 with S_3.

As indicated in Figs. 4-15, 4-17, and 4-18, synchro units can be so connected that one shaft positions itself according to the sum or difference of two other shafts. In these arrangements, two mechanical inputs (shaft positions) produce a mechanical output (shaft position). In some servomechanism applications, however, it is desirable that two mechanical inputs produce an electrical output; that is, an output that would be an electrical signal (error voltage) corresponding to the sum or difference of two mechanical inputs (shaft positions). This can be achieved by substituting a control transformer for the synchro receiver in Fig. 4-15. The induced voltage in the rotor of the control transformer can be made to represent either the sum or difference angle of the two input shafts (transmitter and differential) by appropriate interconnection of the synchro units. The output of the control transformer constitutes an error signal which can be amplified and used to position a load. Load position then becomes a function of the positions of *both* input shafts. In a gun-positioning servomechanism, for example, one input shaft can be controlled by a radar or optical tracker and the other input shaft can represent the lead angle for the target.

4-6. SYNCHRO SYMBOLS AND SIZES

Synchro systems are sometimes classified as either *torque* or *control* systems. A torque synchro system is one that supplies the mechanical power required to position a light load such as an indicator dial. A control synchro system is used to provide electrical information for some other type of load-positioning device, a servomotor for example. In general, control systems are more accurate than torque systems because the mechanical loading on the synchro units is minimized. Synchro units can therefore be classified on the basis of this distinction; for example, torque transmitter, control transmitter, torque receiver, control differential transmitter, and so forth. Letter symbols are often used to identify different types of synchro units as listed below.

TX   — torque transmitter
CX   — control transmitter
TDX — torque differential transmitter
CDX — control differential transmitter
TR   — torque receiver
TDR — torque differential receiver
CT   — control transformer

Some variation in the use of these letter symbols occurs because transmitters and receivers are sometimes referred to as synchro *generators* and *motors* respectively. The letter symbols "G" and "M" may therefore be used to signify these units; for example, "DG" for "differential generator."

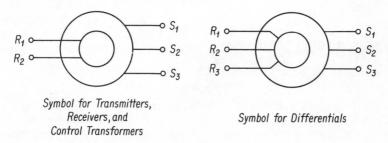

Symbol for Transmitters,
Receivers, and
Control Transformers

Symbol for Differentials

Fig. 4-19 Synchro Schematics

Fig. 4-20 Synchros (Kearfott Division General Precision Inc.)

On schematic diagrams, synchro units are frequently represented by symbols such as those shown in Fig. 4-19. The appropriate letter symbol may be included within the schematic symbol to indicate the specific type of synchro.

Synchro units designed to military standards are assigned type numbers which indicate physical size, type of unit, and excitation frequency. Typical examples of these type numbers are 15CX4, 18TR6, 23TDX6, and 11CT4. The letters in the type designation indicate the function of the synchro unit according to the letter symbols previously listed. The numbers preceding the letters indicate the diameter of the synchro in tenths of an inch, rounded off to the next higher tenth. The number following the letters indicates the excitation frequency for which the unit is designed, 4 for 400 cps and 6 for 60 cps. Synchro type 11CT4 is therefore a control transformer designed for 400 cps operation and is 1.1 in. in diameter. Typical synchro units are shown in Fig. 4-20.

SUMMARY

The synchro transmitter operates as a variable transformer. The rotor winding, functioning as a primary, induces voltage in three stator (secondary) windings positioned 120 deg apart. Since the voltage induced in a secondary winding is determined by the angle at which it is cut by the magnetic field of the primary, the synchro transmitter produces a set of output (stator) voltages that represents the angle of its shaft.

The output voltages of the synchro transmitter are applied to the stator windings of a synchro receiver. A magnetic field is therefore established in the receiver, and the direction of this field is determined by the shaft angle of the transmitter. The receiver shaft now assumes the same angular position as the transmitter shaft. Because the receiver shaft can be positioned by turning the transmitter shaft, the combination of the transmitter and receiver can be used for remote positioning applications. This is a low-torque system suitable only for light loads.

For applications requiring positioning of heavy loads, a synchro control transformer is used instead of the synchro receiver. The control transformer produces an error signal determined by the angular difference of its own shaft and the shaft of the synchro transmitter. This error signal is amplified and drives a servomotor. The motor positions the load and simultaneously rotates the shaft of the control transformer. As this shaft is therefore brought into angular correspondence with the transmitter shaft, the error voltage is reduced to zero and the motor stops.

Synchro differentials are useful in applications requiring that a load be positioned according to the sum (or difference) angle of two shafts.

QUESTIONS

1. In the synchro transmitter, does the rotor or stator function as a transformer primary?

2. When the shaft of a synchro transmitter is at zero degrees, what is the position of the rotor winding with respect to the stators?

3. What is meant by *skew*?

4. Assume that a synchro receiver is connected to a synchro transmitter and that both shafts are at the same angular position. Explain why there is no current flow in the stator windings.

5. When the shaft of a synchro control transformer is at zero degrees, what is the position of the rotor winding with respect to the stators?

6. What is the purpose of a control transformer?

7. Assume that a synchro transmitter, differential, and receiver are connected as shown in Fig. 4-15. If the transmitter shaft is at 310 deg and the differential shaft is at 210 deg, at what angle will the receiver shaft come to rest?

8. In Fig. 4-15, if the transmitter shaft is set to 210 deg and the differential shaft is set to 310 deg, at what angle will the receiver shaft come to rest?

Error Correctors

CHAPTER 5

5-1. INTRODUCTION

Whatever the method used to detect errors in a servomechanism, the error signal is ultimately applied to an error-correcting device. The error corrector then brings the output (load) into correspondence with the command input. To do this, the corrector must be capable of supplying adequate power to the load. It should have a high speed of response (consistent with minimum overshoot), and it should be reversible so that it can correct errors in either direction. The *servomotor* satisfies these requirements and is the most frequently used form of error corrector. Both d-c and a-c servomotors are in use; the choice being made on the basis of load power requirements and the nature of the available voltage source.

5-2. D-C SERVOMOTORS

One form of the d-c motor frequently used in servomechanism applications is the split-field motor. As indicated in Fig. 5-1, this type of motor contains two field windings or, what amounts to the same thing, a center-tapped field winding. One field tends to produce armature rotation in one direction and the other field tends to rotate it in the opposite direction. For reference, the two directions of rotation are identified as *forward* and *reverse* or *counterclockwise* and *clockwise*. The armature of the split-field motor may be connected independently to the d-c supply as shown in Fig. 5-1(A), or it may be connected to the supply through the field windings as in Fig. 5-1(B).

Split-field motors designed to operate at relatively low

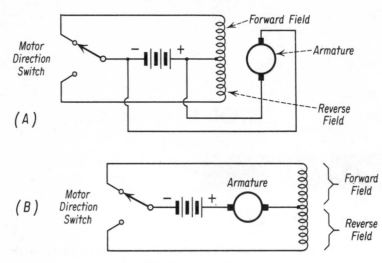

Fig. 5-1   The Split-Field Motor

current may be controlled by vacuum tubes as shown in Fig. 5-2. A balance control is provided to compensate for slight differences in the characteristics of the two tubes so that the plate currents can be adjusted to equal values. With the same amount of current flow through both the forward and the reverse field, the motor is stationary. If an error voltage is now applied to the input terminals of the circuit, the motor will rotate at a speed and in a direction determined by the amplitude and polarity of the error voltage. Assume, for example, that the error voltage is of such polarity that it drives the grid of V_1 positive and the grid of V_2 negative. The plate current of V_1 will now increase and that of V_2 will decrease. Since current flow through the forward field of the motor is now greater than current through the reverse field, the motor rotates in the forward direction. The speed of rotation is determined by the difference of plate currents of the two tubes. A larger amplitude of error voltage, by producing a greater difference of forward and reverse field currents, will cause the motor to rotate faster.

If the error voltage applied to the input terminals of Fig. 5-2 had been of opposite polarity (as compared to that described above), the plate current of V_2 would have been greater than that of V_1. Under these conditions, current through the reverse field would be greater than current through the forward field. This, of course, would cause the motor to rotate in the reverse direction. The polarity of the error voltage therefore determines the direction in

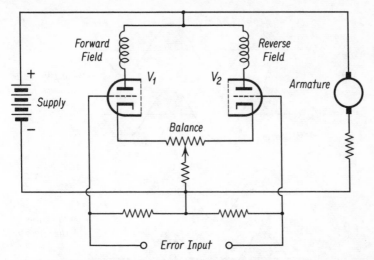

Fig. 5-2 Vacuum Tube Control Circuit for Split-Field Motor

which the motor moves the load. The error detector for this system must be of such design that the polarity of the error voltage will depend upon the direction in which the load has deviated from the desired position.

The use of thyratrons for controlling a split-field motor is illustrated in Fig. 5-3. As in the vacuum tube circuit, one tube supplies current for the forward field and the other tube for the reverse field. An important difference, however, is that the supply voltage is alternating rather than direct. The plates of both thyratrons are positive during one half-cycle of supply, and both negative during the opposite half-cycle. With no error signal applied to the circuit,

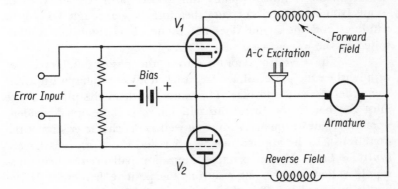

Fig. 5-3 Thyratron Control of Split-Field Motor

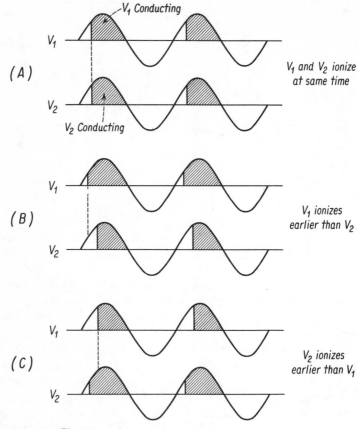

Fig. 5-4 Ionization of Thyratrons in Circuit of Fig. 5-3

the thyratrons conduct equally during the positive half-cycles of supply voltage. Equal currents therefore flow through both field windings and the motor does not rotate. This condition is illustrated by the waveforms in Fig. 5-4(A).

The thyratrons ionize during the positive half-cycles of supply when the plate voltage has reached a value sufficient to overcome the effect of grid bias. The value to which the plate voltage must rise before the thyratrons will ionize is therefore dependent upon the value of the bias supply (as well as the characteristics of the thyratrons). If the applied bias is —5 v and the thyratrons have a *control ratio* of 10, for example, ionization will occur when plate supply voltage reaches 50 v during the positive half-cycle. If the bias is increased to —6 v, the thyratrons will not ionize until plate supply voltage has reached 60 v. The thyratrons can therefore be made to ionize *earlier* or *later* during the positive half-cycles by varying the bias voltage. Once the thyratrons have ionized, they remain ionized for the remainder of the positive half-cycle of supply voltage. This is indicated by the shaded area in the waveforms of Fig. 5-4.

If a d-c error voltage is now applied to the input terminals of Fig. 5-3, one thyratron will ionize earlier than the other. Assume, for example, that the polarity of the error voltage is positive at the grid of V_1 and negative at the grid of V_2. This error voltage has the effect of reducing the bias of V_1 and increasing the bias of V_2. Thyratron V_1 will therefore ionize earlier during the positive alternations because its plate voltage need not rise to as high a value in order to overcome the effect of the bias. Thyratron V_2, however, will ionize later during the positive alternation because its plate voltage must rise to a greater value to overcome the effect of the increased bias. This condition is illustrated by the waveforms in Fig. 5-4(B). During each positive half-cycle of supply voltage, V_1 conducts for a longer time than V_2. The average current through the forward field is therefore greater than that through the reverse field.

If the error voltage had been of opposite polarity (negative at the grid of V_1 and positive at the grid of V_2), the bias of V_2 would be less than the bias of V_1. Thyratron V_2 would consequently ionize earlier than V_1 as shown in Fig. 5-4(C). Since V_2 now conducts for a greater length of time than V_1, the average current through the reverse field exceeds the current through the forward field.

The circuit of Fig. 5-3 will also operate on an a-c phase-reversible error signal such as produced by a synchro control transformer, E transformer, a-c excited potentiometer bridge, and so forth. The error signal is applied through a transformer having a center-tapped secondary, the two halves of the secondary replacing the grid resistors in Fig. 5-3. Depending on whether the error signal is in phase or 180 deg out of phase with the excitation, a positive half cycle of error signal will appear at one thyratron grid and a negative half cycle will appear at the opposite grid (during the positive half-cycle of plate voltage). One thyratron will therefore fire earlier than the other, producing unequal currents through the field windings of the motor. The motor is mechanically coupled back to the error-detector circuit. Rotation of the motor therefore restores the circuit to a condition of balance and reduces the error signal to zero. With no error signal, the thyratrons now conduct equally and the motor stops.

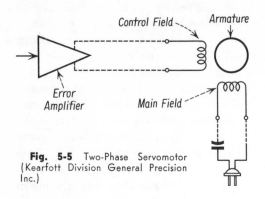

Fig. 5-5 Two-Phase Servomotor (Kearfott Division General Precision Inc.)

5-3. A-C SERVOMOTORS

The two-phase induction motor is used so extensively in servomechanism practice that it has become a standardized component. This motor, also known as a split-phase motor, has two field windings at right angles as shown in Fig. 5-5. The main field, sometimes referred to as a fixed field or reference field, is energized by the excitation supply. The control field, however, receives its input from an error amplifier. Under conditions of zero error in the servomechanism, there is no input to the control field and the motor does not rotate. When an error does occur, however, the amplified error signal appears at the control field of the motor. Since both fields are now energized, the motor rotates. Speed and direction of rotation are dependent upon the amplitude and phase of the error signal.

Proper operation of the motor requires that the two field currents be 90 deg out of phase with each other. These currents produce a rotating magnetic field which "pulls along" the rotor (armature) of the motor. The direction of rotation of the magnetic field (and consequently of the rotor) depends on whether the control field current is 90 deg *ahead* or *behind* the main field current.

Fig. 5-6 shows how a rotating magnetic field is produced by two currents 90 deg out of phase. Here, the two pairs of coils represent the control field and main field of the motor. As indicated by the waveforms in Fig. 5-6(A), the current through the control fields leads the current through the main field by 90 deg. At the instant of time identified as t_1, the control field current is zero and the main field current is maximum. The magnetic field is therefore in the direction indicated by the arrow in Fig. 5-6(B). At a later instant of time (t_2)

the control field and main field currents are of equal amplitude but of opposite polarity. Both fields therefore generate equal magnetic fields, producing a composite field as indicated by the arrow in Fig. 5-6(C). At time t_3, control field current is maximum and main field current is zero. The magnetic field is now in the direction indicated in Fig. 5-6(D). Later, at time t_4, both field currents are equal in amplitude and of the same polarity. The composite magnetic field is now in the direction shown in Fig. 5-6(E).

It should not be assumed that the composite magnetic field rotates in steps. Actually, the rotation is smooth and continuous, passing through the intermediate directions not illustrated in Fig. 5-6. At some instant of time between t_3 and t_4, for example, the direction of the composite field will be somewhere between the directions indicated by the arrows in Figs. 5-6(D) and 5-6(E). Beyond time t_4, the composite field continues its clockwise rotation.

If the control field current had been *lagging* rather than leading the main field current, the rotation of the composite magnetic field would have been in the counterclockwise direction. This is illustrated in Fig. 5-7 in which the direction of the magnetic field is shown for several specific instants of time. Since the field can be made to rotate in either direction, and since the field "pulls" the rotor along with it, the two-phase motor may be regarded as a phase-

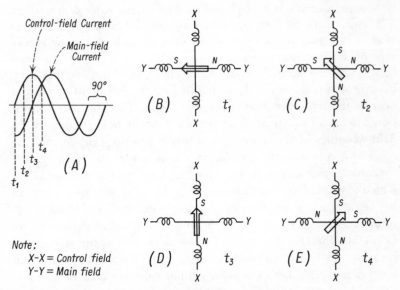

Fig. 5-6 Rotation of Magnetic Field in Two-Phase Servomotor

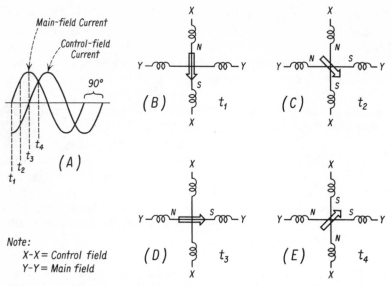

Note:
X-X = Control field
Y-Y = Main field

Fig. 5-7 Counterclockwise Rotation of Magnetic Field

sensitive device: the direction of rotation of the motor can be changed by reversing the phase of the control field excitation.

The rotor or armature of the two-phase motor consists of copper or aluminum bars placed in slots in the rotor laminations. The ends of the bars are connected together by means of a shorting ring at each end of the rotor. As an alternative to this *squirrel-cage* type of construction, a wire-wound rotor may be used (with the ends of the winding shorted together). In either case, the rotating magnetic field cuts across the short-circuited rotor. The resulting current flow in the rotor generates a magnetic field. The magnetized rotor now attempts to align itself with the composite field created by the field windings of the motor. Since this composite field rotates, the rotor also rotates. Actually, the rotor can never "catch up" to the rotating magnetic field. By the time the rotor reaches the position in which it would have been aligned with the composite field, the field has already moved on to a new position. The rotational speed of the rotor is therefore slower than the rotational speed of the composite field—the difference of speed is known as the *slip* of the motor. Slip is characteristic of the two-phase servomotor; it does not result from a deficiency of design. The rotor cannot turn at the same speed as the field because, if it did, it would not be *cut* by the magnetic lines of force. Under these conditions, no current would be induced in the rotor. The rotor would therefore demagnetize and slow down.

The two-phase servomotor is generally used in conjunction with a phase-reversible error detector; for example, differential transformer, synchro control transformer, a-c excited potentiometer bridge, and so forth. These error detectors produce a-c outputs which are either in phase or 180 deg out of phase with excitation, depending upon the direction of error. Since the amplified error voltage is applied to the control field of the servomotor, the direction of rotation of the motor depends upon the direction of the error. This characteristic permits the motor to rotate in the direction required to reduce the error to zero.

The required 90-deg phase difference of the two field currents of the servomotor can be achieved in several ways. One approach is to include a phase-shifting network in the error amplifier. This phasing network, supplemented by any other phase shifts that may occur in the amplifier, causes the control field of the motor to be excited 90 deg out of phase with the main field. Another approach, commonly used in practice, is illustrated in Fig. 5-8(A). Here, a capacitor is connected in series with the main field of the motor. The value of the capacitor is so selected that the capacitive reactance is greater than the inductive reactance of the main field. Current flow through the main field therefore *leads* the excitation voltage. This leading current is represented by vector I_C in Fig. 5-8(B). Since the control field does not have a series capacitor, it constitutes an inductive load on the error amplifier. The current flow through this field therefore lags the error voltage. This lagging current is repre-

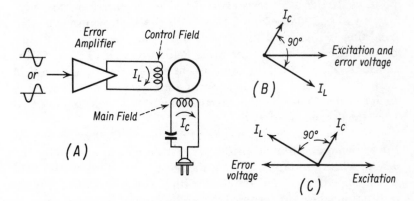

Fig. 5-8 Phase Relationship in Two-Phase Servomotor

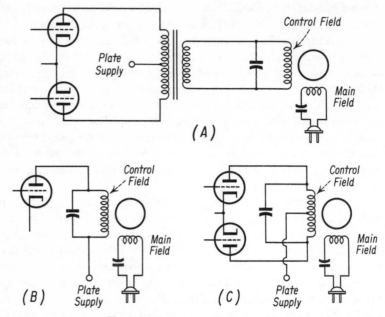

Fig. 5-9 Coupling to Control Field

sented by vector I_L in Fig. 5-8(B). If the value of capacitance in the main field circuit is properly selected, I_L and I_C will be 90 deg out of phase.

The vector diagram in Fig. 5-8(B) assumes that the error signal is *in phase* with the excitation source. This will be the case when the load deviates in a particular direction from the desired position. If the load deviates in the opposite direction, the error signal will be 180 deg out of phase with the excitation source. This condition is illustrated in Fig. 5-8(C). In one case, Fig. 5-8(B), the control field current *lags* the main field current by 90 deg; in the other case, Fig. 5-8(C), the control field current *leads* the main field current by 90 deg. The direction of rotation of the servomotor is therefore determined by the direction in which the load has deviated from the desired position.

The error amplifier may be coupled to the control field of the servomotor through an output transformer as shown in Fig. 5-9(A). This transformer matches the impedance of the control field to the impedance of the amplifier. Either a single-ended or a push-pull output stage may be used, depending upon the power requirements. When space and weight are important considerations, the output transformer may be eliminated as shown in Figs. 5-9(B) and 5-9(C). Here, the control field of the motor is connected directly in the plate circuit of the output stage of the amplifier. The control field is wound for proper impedance match and is insulated to withstand the voltage present in the plate circuit. A center tap on the control field winding is required if the motor is designed for use with a push-pull output stage.

Since current through the output stage may flow in pulses (for example, every other half-cycle), a capacitor is connected across the control field. The capacitor and the control field constitute a *tank* circuit, and the "flywheel effect" restores the missing half-cycles. Current flow through the control field is therefore sinusoidal.

To minimize overshoot and hunting in a servomechanism, some form of *damping* is required. The damper unit is frequently built into the motor housing. One type of damper consists of a paddle wheel in an oil chamber, the paddle wheel being attached to the rotor shaft. Since the paddles must "push against" the oil, the motor is prevented from making any sudden, violent motions such as would produce hunting. Dry friction dampers are also used. A similar effect is achieved by the eddy-current damper. This consists of a cup (or disk) of copper or aluminum mounted on the rotor shaft. The cup is located in the field of a permanent magnet, and current is induced in the cup as it rotates through the magnetic field. This current produces another field of such polarity that it opposes the rotation of the cup. Since the strength of this retarding field depends upon the speed with which the cup cuts the field of the permanent magnet, the retarding force or *drag* is proportional to motor speed. In a variation of this type of damper, the permanent magnet is mounted so that it can rotate. When the servomotor is running at a constant speed, the drag cup and the permanent magnet rotate at the same speed. Since the cup is not *cut* by the magnetic field, no retarding field is generated. If the motor should suddenly attempt to change its speed (or to start from a standstill), the relatively massive permanent magnet cannot change its speed as rapidly as the drag cup. This difference of speed causes the cup to be *cut* by the magnetic field. The retarding force is therefore proportional to acceleration rather than to motor speed.

The effect of a mechanical damper can be simulated electrically. One approach is to couple a small generator to the shaft of the motor. The output of the generator is therefore dependent upon motor speed. The generator voltage is fed back to the error amplifier

Fig. 5-10 Servomotor-Generator
(Thomas A. Edison Industries)

in such polarity that it simulates the retarding force of a damper. The generator, known as a *tachometer generator*, is often built into the servomotor housing as shown in Fig. 5-10.

5-4. INCREMENTAL MOTORS

The incremental motor is a *stepping* device whose shaft rotates a fixed amount each time an input pulse is applied. Shaft position is therefore a function of the number of applied pulses. The size of each step is determined by the design of the motor and may range from a fraction of a degree to a full revolution. By means of a gear train driven by the motor shaft, smaller steps can be obtained.

The steps are established by means of mechanical or electrical detenting; for each applied pulse, the shaft rotates to the next detent position and then stops. Mechanical detenting makes use of a solenoid-operated ratchet or escapement. Electrical detenting is accomplished by means of gear-like teeth on the rotor and field structure so that the rotor stops in a "preferred" position.

An advantage of the incremental motor over the conventional stepless motor is that it requires no power during intervals of zero error. By contrast, one field of the conventional a-c servomotor is continuously energized even when there is no error in the system.

SUMMARY

Servomotors are employed extensively as error correctors. The split-field type is a d-c motor having two opposing field windings which attempt to produce rotation in opposite directions. These fields are connected in the plate circuits of two tubes. An error signal, controlling the bias of the tubes, causes one tube to conduct more than the other and therefore determines the direction of rotation of the motor.

The a-c servomotor (two phase) has two field windings positioned 90 deg apart. When these fields are energized by currents 90 deg out of phase with each other, a rotating magnetic field is established. The rotor is cut by this field and the resulting current flow establishes a magnetic field in the rotor. The rotor therefore turns as it attempts to keep its magnetic field aligned with the rotating field established by the two field windings. A phase reversal of the current through either of the two fields will reverse the direction of rotation of the motor.

A damping device is usually built into the servomotor to minimize overshoot as the motor moves the load to the desired position. The damping can be produced by friction or eddy-current devices.

QUESTIONS

1. Assume that an a-c error signal is applied to the circuit in Fig. 5-3, and explain why the plate supply voltage *must* be a-c rather than d-c.

2. In a two-phase servomotor, what is the required phase relationship of control field current with respect to main field current?

3. Describe the construction of a squirrel-cage type of rotor.

4. In reference to a two-phase servomotor, what is meant by *slip*?

5. What is the purpose of the capacitor usually connected in series with the main field of a two-phase motor?

6. What is the purpose of the capacitor usually connected in parallel with the control field of a two-phase motor?

7. Explain the operation of an eddy-current damper.

Error Amplifiers:
Vacuum Tube

CHAPTER 6

6-1. INTRODUCTION

Error detectors are, in general, low-output devices. Typically, error detector output is in the millivolt or even the microvolt range. Error correctors, however, whether servomotors or solenoid-actuated valves, may require considerable power for proper operation. An amplifier is therefore required to boost the low-level output of the error detector to a power level sufficient to energize the error corrector. The requirements of the error amplifier are:

1. Sufficient voltage gain as determined by the magnitude of the error voltage, and sufficient output as determined by the power requirements of the error corrector.

2. Adequate frequency response over a range determined by the excitation frequency, the rate of change of the command input, and the rate of error change.

3. The ability to amplify the type of signal supplied by the error detector (a-c or d-c) and the ability to supply the type of signal required by the error corrector (a-c or d-c).

To satisfy the last of these requirements, the error amplifier may include a chopper (to convert a d-c error signal to a-c), a demodulator (to convert a-c to d-c) for the error corrector, or both. The amplifier may also include special networks to produce desirable frequency characteristics in the amplifier or to provide a damping effect.

6-2. D-C AMPLIFIERS

Error detectors which produce d-c outputs present a special problem insofar as amplifier design is concerned. Since the error voltage may change at a very slow rate or may remain at zero for long periods of time, the error signal corresponds to an extremely low frequency. Because transformer or R-C-coupled amplifiers are not capable of such low-frequency response, a d-c amplifier is required.

In the direct-coupled amplifier shown in Fig. 6-1, the plate of each stage is resistively coupled to the grid of the following stage. Since there is no coupling capacitor or transformer to provide d-c blocking action, the plate of each stage tends to drive the following grid positive. This tendency is overcome by returning the grid resistors to a negative supply, placing the grid at a negative potential with respect to cathode. The coupling resistor and the grid resistor, however, constitute a voltage divider which attenuates the signal. Additional stages of amplification must be used to compensate for this loss. A more serious disadvantage of the direct-coupled amplifier is its tendency to drift. Changes of supply voltage and variations of part values will produce changes of amplifier output voltage. A change of voltage at the plate of V_1, for example, may result from a change of supply voltage or from a variation of the value of the plate or cathode resistor. The voltage change at the plate of V_1 causes a change of bias at the grid of V_2, producing a change at the plate of V_2 and the grid of V_3, and so forth. A small change of voltage

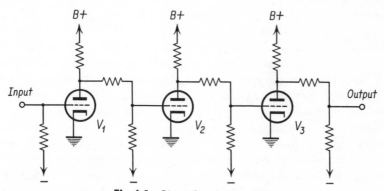

Fig. 6-1   Direct-Coupled Amplifier

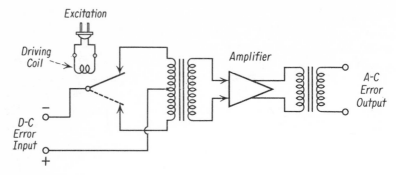

Fig. 6-2 The Chopper Amplifier

in the first stage can therefore produce a large change of amplifier output voltage. As a result, the output of the amplifier may not be zero even when there is no input (error) applied to the amplifier. Since the amplifier is unable to distinguish between error-produced changes and changes resulting from supply or temperature variations, excellent power supply regulation and highly stable circuit components are essential. Because it is so critical with respect to temperature and supply variations, the direct-coupled amplifier is used only to a limited extent. As an alternative, the chopper amplifier is employed. In this type of circuit, the d-c error voltage is converted to a corresponding a-c signal, permitting the use of transformer or *R-C* coupling between stages.

6-3. CHOPPER AMPLIFIERS

The *chopper* is an electromechanical device sometimes referred to as a *vibrator* or *contact modulator*. Sine-wave excitation applied to the driving coil of the chopper causes a metal reed to vibrate between two fixed contacts. As shown in Fig. 6-2, the contacts are connected to opposite ends of the primary of a transformer. The d-c input voltage (error) is applied between the reed and the center tap of the transformer. As the reed vibrates, it connects the error voltage alternately to the opposite ends of the transformer winding. When the reed is in the upper position in Fig. 6-2, the error voltage causes current flow in a *downward* direction through the upper half of the transformer winding. A short time later the reed is in the lower position and current flows *upward* through the lower half of the transformer winding. This periodic reversal of current direction through the primary of the transformer causes an alternating voltage to be induced in the secondary. The chopper waveform is essentially a square wave as indicated in Fig. 6-3. The amplitude and phase of the square wave are dependent on the amplitude and polarity of the d-c error voltage. As shown in Fig. 6-3, a reduction of d-c error voltage results in a reduction of square-wave amplitude. A change of polarity of the d-c error voltage produces a change of phase of the square wave. The length of time the vibrating reed rests on the fixed contact is known as the *dwell* time. During the time required for the reed to move from one contact to the other, no current flows through the primary.

After the d-c error voltage has been converted to an a-c

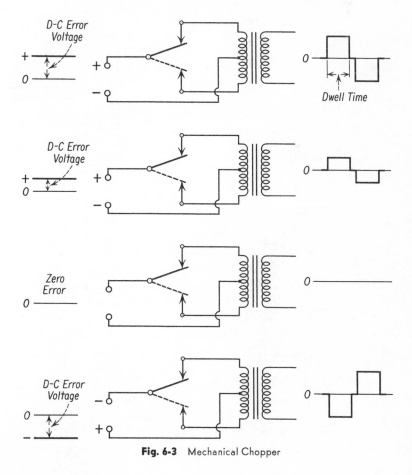

Fig. 6-3 Mechanical Chopper

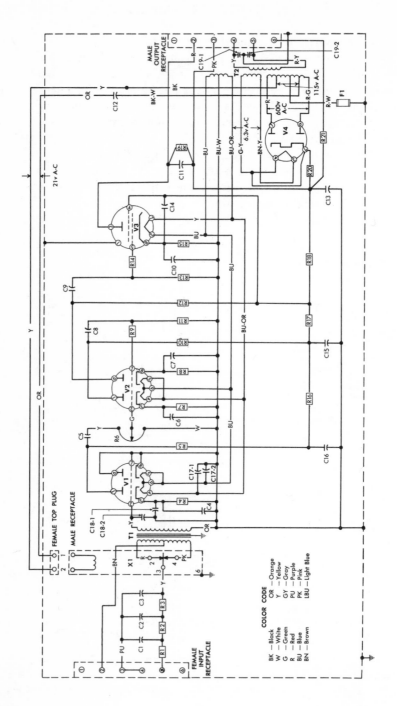

Fig. 6-4 Chopper Amplifier Circuit (Leeds and Northrup Co.)

PARTS LIST FOR FIG. 6-4

★ RESISTORS

			Part No.
R1	2000Ω	1W	011515
R2	2000Ω		11-4-0-95
R3	2000Ω		11-4-0-95
R4	10000Ω		11-1-0-56
R5	1.0 Meg.		11-1-0-80
R6	1.0 Meg.		Std. 3246-166
R7	10000Ω		11-1-0-56
R8	10000Ω		11-1-0-56
R9	2.2 Meg.		11-1-0-84
R10	1.0 Meg.		11-1-0-80
R11	1.0 Meg.		11-1-0-80
R12	1.0 Meg.		11-1-0-80
R13	1.0 Meg.		11-1-0-80
R14	10000Ω		11-1-0-56
R15	390Ω	2W	11-3-0-39
R16	0.1 Meg.		11-1-0-68
R17	0.1 Meg.		11-1-0-68
R18	10000Ω	1W	11-2-0-56
R19	1.0 Meg.		11-1-0-80
R20	300Ω	10W	011059
R21	22000Ω	2W	11-3-0-60

★ Resistors are ½ watt with ± 10% tolerance except as specified.

CAPACITORS

				Part No.
C1	8μf	5v	DC	⎫
C2	8μf	5v	DC	⎬ R-820-L
C3	8μf	5v	DC	⎭
C4	50μf	25v	DC	Std. 2645-53
C5	0.022μf	400v	DC	23-3-0-20
C6	50μf	25v	DC	Std. 2645-53
C7	50μf	25v	DC	Std. 2645-53
C8	0.022μf	400v	DC	23-3-0-20
C9	0.022μf	400v	DC	23-3-0-20
C10	50μf	25v	DC	Std. 2645-53
C11	1.0μf	600v	DC	⎫ R-820-K
C12	0.5μf	600v	DC	⎭
C13	4μf	450v	DC	Std. 2645-52
C14	4μf	450v	DC	Std. 2645-52
C15	4μf	450v	DC	Std. 2645-52
C16	4μf	450v	DC	Std. 2645-52
C17-1	0.001μf			⎫ 023125
C17-2	0.001μf			⎭
C18-1	0.001μf			⎫ 023125
C18-2	0.001μf			⎭
C19-1	0.001μf			⎫ 023125
C19-2	0.001μf			⎭

MISCELLANEOUS

		Part No.
V1	12AX7 Tube	22-1-0-6
V2	12AX7 Tube	22-1-0-6
V3	6L6 Tube	Std. 3246-178
V4	6X4 Tube	22-3-0-1
X1	Converter	Std. 3338-1
T1	Input Transformer	Std. 21178-39
T2	Power Transformer	Std. 21178-40
F1	3/16 Amp. Slo-Blo Fuse	14-5-0-1

signal it can be applied to a conventional amplifier using either transformer or *R-C* coupling. The a-c output of the error amplifier is applied to the error corrector: the control field of an a-c servomotor, for example.

The chopper amplifier shown in Fig. 6-4 is used in the Leeds and Northrup *Speedomax*® recorder. Voltage derived from a potentiometer connected to a standard cell is applied between terminals 2 and 3 of the input receptacle. The input voltage to be measured and recorded (from a thermocouple, for example) is applied between terminals 4 and 5 of the same receptacle. A low-pass filter connected to these terminals removes the stray pickup that may be present on the thermocouple leads.

When the circuit is at balance, the potentiometer voltage (terminals 2 and 3) exactly cancels the thermocouple voltage (terminals 4 and 5) and there is no input to the chopper. Lack of balance however, produces an error voltage that is applied between the reed of the chopper and the center tap of the input transformer. The resulting a-c signal is amplified and used to excite the control field of a two-phase servomotor. This field is connected between terminals 2 and 3 of the output receptacle and is therefore in the plate circuit of tube V_3. The servomotor is mechanically coupled to the pointer of an indicator, to a pen that writes on a motor-driven paper chart, and to the balancing potentiometer that restores the circuit to balance. The sensitivity of the circuit is adjusted by means of a gain control (R_6) in the grid circuit of V_2. This control is adjusted to eliminate hunting. Power transformer T_2 supplies the input power for the driving coil of the chopper and for the full-wave rectifier (V_4) which provides the B voltages for the amplifier.

When a chopper amplifier is to feed into a d-c type of error corrector, a demodulator must be used to change the amplified a-c error signal into a corresponding d-c error signal. Another chopper (or another reed and set of contacts on the same chopper) can be used for the demodulation process. As shown in Fig. 6-5, the fixed contacts of the demodulator are connected to opposite ends of the secondary of the output transformer. The driving coil for the de-modulator reed is excited by the same source that drives the input chopper (or both reeds are driven by the same coil). The two reeds therefore move in synchronism. Since the demodulator reed vibrates at the same rate that the a-c error voltage changes polarity (determined by the rate of the input reed) a d-c voltage appears at the demodulator reed. When the upper end of the secondary winding is positive, as in Fig. 6-5(A), the demodulator reed is in the upper position. During the opposite half-cycle of the chopped error voltage, the lower end of the secondary is positive as indicated in Fig. 6-5(B). At this time, the demodulator reed is in the down position and is therefore still at a positive potential. The capacitor connected to the demodulator reed functions as a filter to smooth the voltage variations (otherwise the output voltage would decrease to zero during the time the demodulator reed moves from one contact to the other). The voltage across the filter capacitor is therefore an amplified equivalent of the d-c error voltage applied to the input chopper. When the input error voltage varies, the output voltage across the filter capacitor varies in a corresponding manner. If the error input voltage should reverse in polarity (when the load deviates in the opposite direction from the desired position), the voltage across the filter capacitor will also reverse in polarity. This is illustrated in Figs. 6-5(C) and 6-5(D).

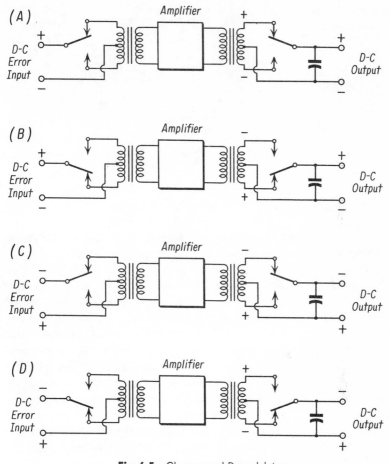

Fig. 6-5 Chopper and Demodulator

Here, the demodulator reed arrives at each fixed contact at a time when the corresponding end of the secondary winding is negative. Output voltage, like the error input voltage, is therefore of negative polarity.

Electronic Modulators and Demodulators

The chopping and demodulation functions can be performed in purely electronic circuits. Such circuits do not involve mechanically moving parts as does the vibrator type of chopper. Life expectancy is therefore greater. Noise level, however, will generally be higher.

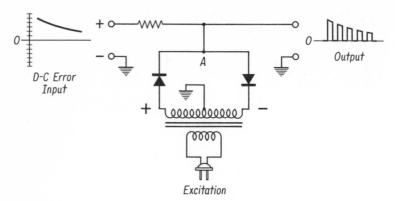

Fig. 6-6 Electronic Chopper

An electronic chopper or modulator is shown in Fig. 6-6. During the half-cycle of excitation voltage when transformer polarity is as shown, both diodes become conductive. Assuming that the diodes have equivalent forward resistances, point A is now at the same potential as the tap of the transformer (ground). During the opposite half-cycle of excitation voltage, the diodes are reverse biased and therefore nonconductive. Point A is now effectively disconnected from the transformer and is therefore at the same potential as the input terminal (the applied d-c error voltage). In this manner, point A alternates between two voltage levels: ground and the d-c error voltage. Since point A is the output terminal, output voltage is a square wave at the frequency of the excitation voltage and having an amplitude excursion from ground to the value of the d-c error voltage. Should the error voltage change in magnitude, the square-wave output will vary correspondingly in amplitude. Should the d-c error voltage reverse in polarity, the output square wave would extend from ground to a negative level equal to the d-c error voltage. The excitation voltage should be larger in amplitude than the d-c error voltage so that the error voltage will not upset the biasing of the diodes.

Another electronic chopper, sometimes called a ring modulator, is shown in Fig. 6-7. During the half-cycle of excitation when the polarity of transformer T_1 is as shown, diodes D_1 and D_2 are conductive. Point A is therefore at the same potential as the center tap of T_1 (error voltage). The d-c error voltage is now effectively connected to point A and to the upper end of transformer T_2. During the opposite half-cycle of excitation, diodes D_3 and D_4 become conductive. Point B is now at the same potential as the center tap of T_1. At this time, the d-c error input is effectively connected to the lower end of transformer T_2. In this manner, the d-c error input is alternately transferred between the upper and lower ends of transformer T_2 (as would be the case with a vibrating reed performing the switching action). The secondary voltage of T_2 is therefore an a-c signal corresponding to the d-c error input.

An electronic *demodulator* is shown in Fig. 6-8. Circuits of this type are also known as *phase-sensitive detectors* because the polarity of the d-c output voltage depends upon the phase of the a-c input (error) signal. Both diodes in Fig. 6-8(A) conduct during the half-cycle of excitation when the polarity of transformer T_1 is as shown. The diodes do not conduct equally, however, because of the a-c error voltage applied to transformer T_2. When the induced voltage in the secondary of this transformer has the polarity shown, the voltage in the upper half of the secondary adds to the secondary voltage of T_1. The voltage in the lower half of the secondary subtracts from (bucks) the voltage in the secondary of T_1. As a result, diode D_1 conducts more current than diode D_2. A greater charge therefore builds up on capacitor C_1 than on capacitor C_2. Since the d-c output voltage is equal to the difference of these charges, the polarity of the output is as shown in Fig. 6-8(A).

If the a-c error signal applied to transformer T_2 had

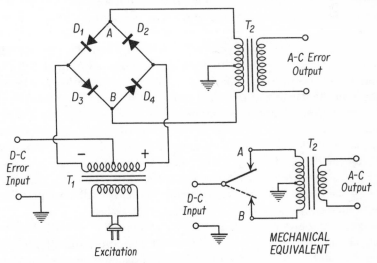

Fig. 6-7   The Ring Modulator

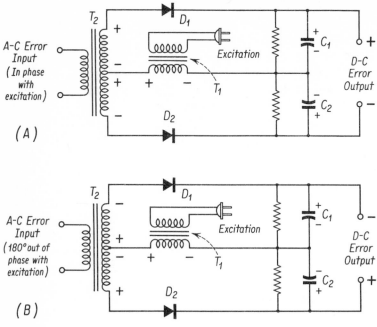

Fig. 6-8 Phase-Sensitive Detector

been of opposite phase, as shown in Fig. 6-8(B), diode D_2 would conduct more current than diode D_1. As a result, the charge on capacitor C_2 would exceed that of C_1. The d-c output voltage would therefore be of opposite polarity as compared to Fig. 6-8(A).

During the half-cycles of excitation when the polarity of transformer T_1 is opposite that shown in Figs. 6-8(A) and 6-8(B), neither diode conducts. Capacitors C_1 and C_2, functioning as filters, maintain the d-c output essentially constant during these half-cycles. The excitation voltage in the secondary of transformer T_1 should be greater in amplitude than the voltage induced in the halves of the secondary of T_2. If this is not the case, one of the diodes will conduct during the half-cycle of excitation when the polarity of T_1 is opposite that shown in Fig. 6-8. Such conduction will alter the charge on one of the capacitors and the difference of charge will no longer be an accurate representation of the amount of error.

In the demodulator circuit shown in Fig. 6-9, diodes D_1 and D_2 conduct during one half-cycle of excitation and diodes D_3 and D_4 conduct during the opposite half-cycle. When the polarity of T_1 is such that diodes D_1 and D_2 are conductive, point A is at the

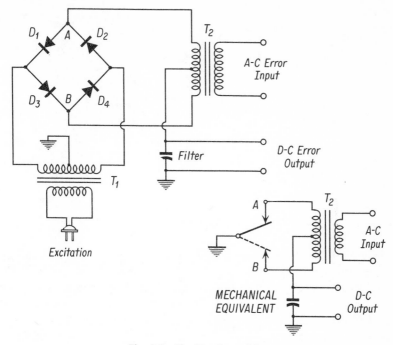

Fig. 6-9   The Ring Demodulator

same potential as the center tap of T_1 (ground). When the polarity of T_1 reverses, diodes D_3 and D_4 conduct, and point B is now at ground potential. The upper and lower ends of the secondary of T_2 are therefore alternately at ground potential. For this reason, a d-c charge builds up on the filter capacitor even though the input to T_2 is a-c.

6-4. A-C AMPLIFIERS

Servomechanisms employing an error detector that produces a-c output and an error corrector that requires a-c input do not need modulators or demodulators. The a-c signal from the error detector is applied to a transformer-coupled or R-C-coupled amplifier where it is amplified to a level sufficient to drive the error corrector. A representative circuit of this type is shown in Fig. 6-10. The output from an a-c-excited error detector is coupled to the grid of V_1. The a-c error signal may be either in phase or 180 deg out of phase with the excitation voltage, depending upon the direction of

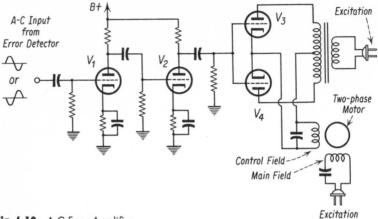

Fig. 6-10 A-C Error Amplifier

error in the servomechanism. After two stages of R-C-coupled amplification (V_1 and V_2) the error signal is applied to the grids of V_3 and V_4. Tubes V_3 and V_4 operate with a-c plate voltage. Since the plates of these two tubes are connected to opposite ends of the excitation transformer, they are supplied with voltages 180 deg out of phase; that is, the plate of V_1 is positive when the plate of V_2 is negative and vice versa. For this reason, only one of the two plates can be positive during the positive alternation of grid (error) signal.

In Fig. 6-11(A), the phase of the error signal is such that a positive alternation appears at the grids of V_3 and V_4 during the half-cycle when the plate of V_3 is positive. Since its grid and plate are both positive, V_3 conducts. Tube V_4 cannot conduct because its plate is negative at this time. A half-cycle later, a negative alternation of error signal appears at both grids and neither V_3 nor V_4 can conduct. Tube V_3 therefore conducts only if the error signal is in phase with the excitation source and only during the positive half-cycles of plate supply voltage.

If the error signal had been 180 deg out of phase with the excitation source, tube V_4 would conduct instead of V_3. This is indicated in Fig. 6-11(B). Here, the plate of V_4 is positive during the positive alternation of error signal at the grids. The control field of the two-phase servomotor (Fig. 6-10) is energized by the plate current of V_3 or V_4 (whichever is conductive). Since the plate voltages of these two tubes are 180 deg out of phase with each other, the control field of the motor is excited either 90 deg *ahead* or 90 deg *behind* the main field excitation. The direction of rotation of the

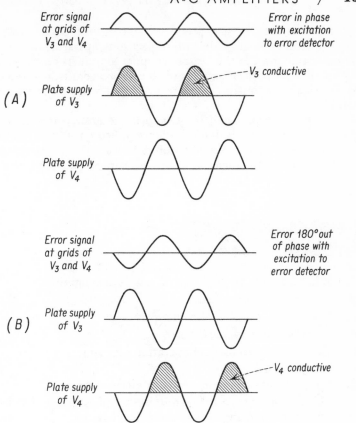

Error signal
at grids of
V_3 and V_4

Error in phase
with excitation
to error detector

(A)

Plate supply
of V_3

V_3 conductive

Plate supply
of V_4

Error signal
at grids of
V_3 and V_4

Error 180° out
of phase with
excitation to
error detector

(B)

Plate supply
of V_3

Plate supply
of V_4

V_4 conductive

Fig. 6-11   Waveforms for Circuit of Fig. 6-10

motor therefore depends upon the phase of the error signal. The capacitor connected across the control field produces a "flywheel effect" to restore the missing half-cycles. Control field current is therefore sinusoidal rather than half-wave.

SUMMARY

The servoamplifier must have sufficient gain to respond to the low-level signal from the error detector, and must provide sufficient power output to drive the error corrector.

Direct-coupled amplifier stages may be used in conjunction

with an error detector that produces a d-c output. Such amplifiers, however, tend to be unstable with respect to temperature and supply voltage variations. For this reason, chopper amplifiers are frequently employed. The chopper converts the d-c error signal to a corresponding a-c signal, permitting the use of *R-C-* or transformer-coupled amplifier stages.

If the error signal is a-c, and if the error corrector is of a type that requires d-c excitation, the amplified error signal must be changed back to d-c. A demodulator is used for this purpose. Choppers and demodulators may be either mechanical (vibrating reed) or electronic.

QUESTIONS

1. What is meant by *drift* in a direct-coupled amplifier?
2. Name two causes of drift.
3. What is the purpose of a chopper?
4. What is meant by *dwell time?*
5. Explain the purpose and operation of a vibrating reed demodulator.
6. Is the output of a phase-sensitive detector a-c or d-c?
7. What change occurs in the output of a phase-sensitive detector when the input signal is reversed in phase?
8. In reference to Fig. 6-10, explain how the servomotor reverses direction when the error signal reverses in phase.

Error Amplifiers: Transistor

CHAPTER 7

7-1. TRANSISTOR FUNDAMENTALS

In servomechanisms, as in other types of electronic apparatus, the transistor offers the advantages of small size and weight, low
power requirements, and long life expectancy. Transistor amplifiers
are therefore frequently used in preference to vacuum tube amplifiers, particularly when size and weight are primary considerations.

The transistor is a semiconductor device (germanium or
silicon) in which the output current is controlled by input current.
Pure germanium (or silicon) is not used in the transistor. Rather,
chemical ingredients known as *impurities* are added to produce
either *N*-type or *P*-type semiconductor. In *N*-type semiconductor
some of the electrons are relatively free to move out of their atomic
orbits and can therefore act as *carriers* of electric current. In *P*-type
semiconductor, the atomic structure is incomplete in the sense that
there are vacancies in some of the orbits. These vacancies are known
as *holes* and an electron can move through the *P*-type semiconductor
by moving from hole to hole (as a person entering a crowded auditorium might take a seat at the back and then gradually progress
toward the front by moving into the seats left vacant by other per-
sons leaving the auditorium). All other factors being equal, an electron can move more rapidly through *N*-type than through *P*-type
semiconductor. In *P*-type semiconductor, the electron cannot make
its move until a hole appears in its vicinity as a result of another
electron having moved away (in the same way that the person in the
crowded auditorium cannot move ahead until another person decides
to leave).

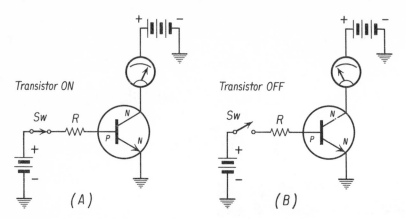

Fig. 7-1 Supply Polarities for **NPN** Transistor

In the transistor, the same type of semiconductor is used for both the emitter and collector but the opposite type is used for the base. In the *NPN* transistor, for example, the emitter and collector are both *N*-type and the base is *P*-type semiconductor. In the *PNP* transistor, the emitter and collector are *P*-type and the base is *N*-type semiconductor. As indicated in Fig. 7-1, the collector circuit is reverse biased: the *N*-type collector is connected to the positive terminal of the supply. If a *PNP* transistor had been used, the *P*-type collector would have been connected to the negative terminal of the supply.

In Fig. 7-1(A), the input element (base) is forward biased: positive input to *P*-type semiconductor. As a result, the transistor is *on*, or conductive, and current flows in the collector circuit. If the switch is opened, as in Fig. 7-1(B), the positive input is removed from the *P*-type base. Since the base is no longer forward biased, the transistor is *off*, or nonconductive. Resistor *R* limits the base current (when the switch is closed) and therefore determines the extent to which the transistor is turned *on*. If this resistance is decreased, for example, the transistor will be more fully *on*, and collector current will increase. If the value of *R* is increased, the transistor operating point will be shifted toward *off*, and collector current will decrease. Since the amount of output (collector) current is determined by the amount of input (base) current, the ratio of these currents expresses the gain of the transistor. This current gain is known as the *beta* of the transistor and is numerically equal to the *change of collector current* divided by the *change of base current.*

The relationships described above also apply to the *PNP* transistor except that supply polarities are reversed. As shown in Fig. 7-2, a negative input applied to the *N*-type base will turn *on* the transistor. When the switch is opened, the negative input is removed from the *N*-type semiconductor. Since the base is no longer forward biased, the transistor turns *off*.

Even when the forward bias is removed from the input (base) of the transistor, as in Figs. 7-1(B) and 7-2(B), some small amount of current still flows in the collector circuit. This current, variously referred to as *leakage,* collector cutoff current, or I_{co}, varies with temperature. Because of the temperature coefficient of the semiconductor, an increase of temperature produces an increase in the value of leakage current. The increased leakage current, however, further heats the transistor and produces a still greater increase of leakage current. Such *thermal runaway* can destroy the transistor. To prevent this condition and to stabilize the operating point of the transistor with respect to temperature changes, a resistor can be connected in the emitter lead. This is shown in Fig. 7-3. A voltage drop is produced across this resistor by the leakage current of the transistor, and the polarity of the voltage is positive at the *N*-type emitter. As a result of this reverse bias, the transistor operating point is shifted toward *off*. If the temperature of the transistor should now increase, the leakage current will tend to increase and the voltage drop across the stabilizing resistor will also increase. This increase of reverse bias at the emitter will now reduce the leakage current. In this manner, the leakage current is prevented from rising to a

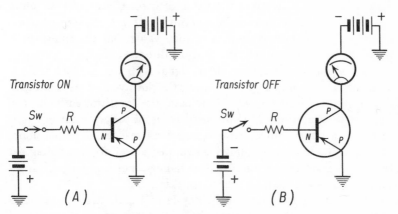

Fig. 7-2 Supply Polarities for **PNP** Transistor

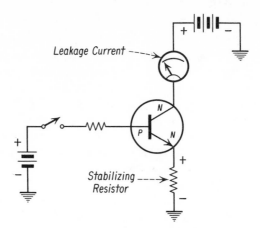

Fig. 7-3 Temperature Stabilization

value that would drastically change the operating point or even destroy the transistor.

7-2. *TRANSISTOR AMPLIFIERS*

A practical transistor amplifier stage is shown in Fig. 7-4. This circuit employs a single supply rather than two separate supplies as in Fig. 7-1. Forward bias for the base is obtained through a voltage divider (R_1 and R_2) connected across the collector supply source. Resistor R_2 is sometimes omitted and R_1 then functions simply as a base-current-limiting resistor. The value of R_1 (and of R_2 if it is used) determines the value of base current and therefore the extent to which the transistor is turned *on*. For class A operation of the stage, the base resistor is of such value that the transistor is partially *on*: half way betwen *off* and full *on*.

Assume now that an input signal is applied to the transistor amplifier as shown in Fig. 7-4. During the positive half-cycle of input signal (positive input to the *P*-type base) the transistor shifts toward the full *on* condition. The increased value of collector current now produces a larger voltage drop across load resistor R_3. Since more of the available supply voltage is dropped across R_3, the voltage at the collector decreases. The positive half-cycle of input signal therefore produces a negative-going output signal.

During the negative half-cycle of input, the forward bias of the base decreases. Transistor operation therefore shifts toward *off* and collector current decreases. Since the drop across R_3 is now smaller than previously, the voltage at the collector rises. The negative half-cycle of input therefore produces a positive half-cycle of output signal. Input and output signals are therefore 180 deg out of phase. This is characteristic of the common emitter amplifier, the type shown in Fig. 7-4.

The emitter resistor, R_4 in Fig. 7-4, introduces degeneration if it is not bypassed (as does a cathode resistor in a vacuum tube circuit). During the positive half-cycle of input signal, for example, collector current increases. The increased current however, produces a greater voltage drop across R_4. This voltage, positive at the N-type emitter, limits the increase of collector current. As a result of this degeneration, the collector current does not increase as much as it would have if the emitter had been grounded directly. Such limitation of the excursion of collector current reduces the amplitude of the output signal; that is, reduces the gain of the stage. A capacitor may be connected across the emitter resistor as indicated by the dotted line in Fig. 7-4. The capacitor keeps the voltage across R_4 constant, preventing this voltage from following the variations of the input signal. Because emitter voltage cannot rise and fall to oppose changes of collector current, degeneration does not occur and stage gain is increased.

Although degeneration reduces gain, it does improve the circuit performance in other ways. Degeneration reduces distortion and also stabilizes the circuit so that gain remains essentially constant regardless of (1) supply voltage variations, (2) parts value

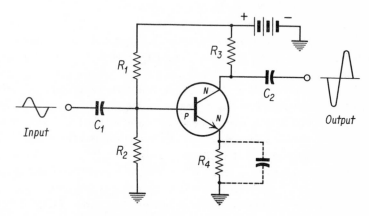

Fig. 7-4 Common-Emitter Transistor Amplifier

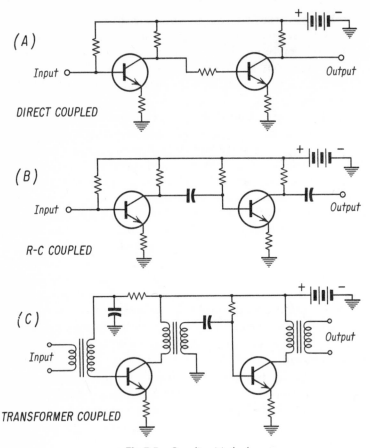

Fig 7-5 Coupling Methods

changes, and (3) aging or replacement of transistors. To achieve these advantages of circuit performance, some designers intentionally omit the emitter bypass capacitor.

In the transistor amplifier, the coupling capacitors are large in value as compared to those used in vacuum tube amplifiers. Because the input impedance of a vacuum tube is relatively high, most of the input signal appears across this impedance and relatively little signal is dropped across the reactance of the coupling capacitor. The transistor, however, has a relatively low input impedance. Less signal is therefore developed across this low impedance, and more signal is dropped across the reactance of the coupling capacitor. To minimize this signal loss, the reactance of the coupling capacitor should be small as compared to the input impedance of the transistor. It is for this reason that the coupling capacitors of a transistor amplifier are large in value. Typical values are in the range of 2 to 20 μf, depending upon the desired low-frequency response.

Transistor amplifier stages connected in cascade may be direct coupled, *R-C* coupled, or transformer coupled, as shown in Fig. 7-5. As in the case of vacuum tube circuits, direct coupling offers the advantage of extended low-frequency response all the way down to zero cycles per second (d-c). Drift, however, is a problem. Transformer or *R-C* coupling eliminates this problem at the expense of increased circuit complexity (more components) and limited low-frequency response. *NPN* transistors are shown in Fig. 7-5, but *PNP* types may be used if supply polarity is reversed. Two varieties of transformer coupling are illustrated in Fig. 7-5(C). In the first stage, the base current of the transistor flows through the secondary winding of the transformer. This current may saturate the iron core of the transformer, particularly if the transformer is a miniature type. To prevent this, a blocking capacitor may be used as in the second stage of Fig. 7-5(C). Here, only the a-c signal current flows through the secondary.

The amplifiers shown in Figs. 7-4 and 7-5 are *common-emitter* circuits: the input signal is applied to the base, the output is taken from the collector, and the emitter is common to both input

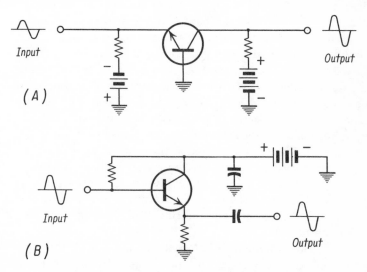

Fig. 7-6 Common-Base and Common-Collector Amplifiers

CIRCUIT CONFIGURATION	CHARACTERISTICS*
COMMON EMITTER (CE)	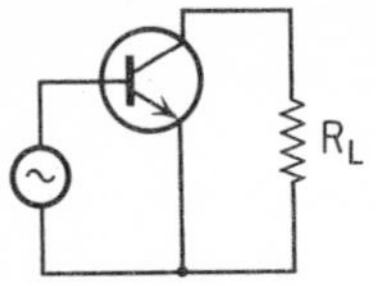 moderate input impedance (1.3 K) moderate output impedance (50 K) high current gain (35) high voltage gain (−270) highest power gain (40 db)
COMMON BASE (CB)	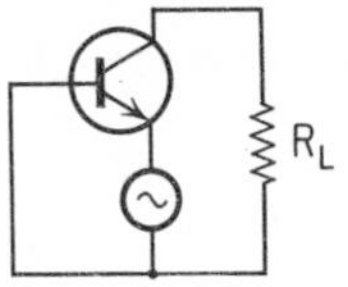 lowest input impedance (35 Ω) highest output impedance (1 M) low current gain (−0.98) high voltage gain (380) moderate power gain (26 db)
COMMON COLLECTOR (CC) (EMITTER FOLLOWER)	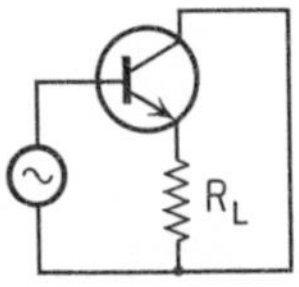 highest input impedance (350 K) lowest output impedance (500 Ω) high current gain (−36) unity voltage gain (1.00) lowest power gain (15 db)

*Numerical values are typical for the 2N525 at audio frequencies with a bias of 5v and 1ma, a load resistance of 10K, and a source (generator) resistance of 1K

Fig. 7-7 Transistor Amplifier Characteristics

and output circuits. A *common-base* circuit is shown in Fig. 7-6(A). Here, the input signal is applied to the emitter, the output is taken from the collector, and the base is common (signal ground). This circuit does not invert the signal polarity as does the common-emitter amplifier. The negative half-cycle of input signal, for example, will drive the transistor toward full *on* (negative input to *N*-type emitter). As a result, collector current increases, more voltage is dropped across the load resistor, and collector voltage decreases. The negative alternation of input therefore produces a negative-going output. The input impedance of the common-base circuit is lower and the output impedance is higher as compared to the common-emitter circuit. For the common-base configuration, the ratio of output (collector) current to input (emitter) current expresses the current gain of the transistor. This current gain is known as *alpha* and is numerically equal to the *change of collector current* divided by the *change of emitter current.*

In the *common-collector* circuit, Fig. 7-6(B), the input signal is applied to the base, the output is taken from the emitter, and the collector is common (signal ground). Because of its resemblance to the vacuum tube cathode follower, this circuit is often referred to as an *emitter follower.* The voltage gain of the emitter follower, like that of the cathode follower, is less than unity. This loss of signal amplitude is tolerated in those applications requiring the use of a stage with high input impedance (to minimize the loading on the preceding stage). The emitter follower produces no reversal of signal polarity. A positive half-cycle of input signal (to the *P*-type base in Fig. 7-6) drives the transistor toward full *on.* The increased current flow now produces a larger voltage drop across the emitter load resistor. Output therefore becomes more positive during the positive alternation of input signal.

The characteristics of the common-emitter (CE), common-base (CB), and common-collector (CC) circuits are tabulated in Fig. 7-7. The diagrams shown are *signal circuits;* that is, the supply sources are not shown.

7-3. SERVOAMPLIFIERS

A transistor amplifier designed to drive a 2-w servomotor is shown in Fig. 7-8. The circuit is designed for a 400-cps error signal and will operate over an ambient temperature range of —55 to 125 C. Transistors Q_1, Q_2, and Q_3 and associated circuit components constitute a *preamplifier*, Q_4 and Q_5 comprise the *driver*, and Q_6 and Q_7 are used in the *output* stage.

Transistors Q_1 and Q_2 are connected as common-emitter amplifiers, Q_1 being directly coupled to Q_2. Temperature stabilization of these two stages is provided by emitter resistors R_2 and R_5, and gain stabilization is achieved by degenerative (negative) feedback from the emitter of Q_2 to the base of Q_1. Transistor Q_2 is capacitively coupled to Q_3 which is also connected as a common-emitter stage. Direct coupling is used between Q_3 and Q_4 and resistor R_{10} provides negative feedback to Q_3.

Transistors Q_4 and Q_5 provide push-pull signals for the output stage. Q_4 functions as an emitter follower whose output is coupled to the emitter of Q_5. Q_5 operates as a common-base stage. In this combination (an emitter follower feeding into a common-base amplifier), the collector currents of the two transistors vary in opposite directions; that is, when the collector current of Q_4 *increases*, the collector current of Q_5 *decreases*. During the positive half-cycle of error signal at the base of Q_4, for example, the collector current of

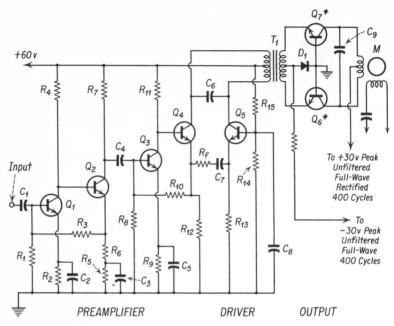

Fig. 7-8   Transistor Amplifier for Two-Watt Servomotor (General Electric Co.)

R_1——————24K	C_4,C_6——————10μf	
R_2——————4.7K	C_8——————6μf	
R_3,R_{11}——————22K	Q_1,Q_2,Q_3—GE 2N335 OR GE 2N336	
R_4——————51K	Q_4,Q_5——————GE 2N656A	
R_5,R_9——————10K	Q_6,Q_7——GE 2N497A OR GE 2N498A	
R_6——————180Ω	T_1——————12.5:1 Step Down	
R_7——————39K	D_1——————GE 1N676	
R_8——————15K	NOTES:	
R_{10}——————9.1K	1. ★ Heat Sink Q_6 and Q_7	
R_{12}——————2.7K	2. Adjust R_F for Desired Gain.	
R_{13},R_{14}——————2.4K	3. C_9 Adjusted to Tune Motor	
R_{15}——————3.6K	for Maximum Stalled Torque.	
C_1,C_2,C_3,C_5,C_7——20μf	4. C_6 Adjusted to Tune T_1.	

Q_4 will *increase*. The positive alternation of signal is coupled from the emitter of Q_4 to the emitter of Q_5. Since the emitter of Q_5 is N-type semiconductor, Q_5 is driven toward *off*, and its collector current *decreases*. Current flow through half of the primary of transformer T_1 therefore increases, and current through the other half decreases. The primary winding of T_1 is tuned by capacitor C_6.

Transistors Q_6 and Q_7 function as push-pull, common-base amplifiers. The emitters receive their inputs from opposite ends of the secondary of T_1, and the collectors are connected to opposite ends of the tapped control field of the servomotor. The main field of the motor is supplied through a phase-shifting capacitor from the 400-cps source. Collector and emitter supply voltages are obtained from full-wave unfiltered rectifier circuits operating from the 400-cps supply. The use of unfiltered supply voltage reduces transistor dissipation. Both output transistors are mounted on heat sinks (copper or aluminum heat-radiating surfaces).

The negative unfiltered supply provides forward bias for the N-type emitters, and the transistors are therefore partially *on*. During large-amplitude input signals, the voltage induced in the secondary of T_1 causes diode D_1 to conduct. The conducting diode shunts out the negative supply voltage, allowing transistor operation to shift in the direction of *off*.

A transistor amplifier used in the Taylor Instrument Co. TRANSCOPE® recorder is shown in Fig. 7-9. The amplifier is divided into three sections: impedance-matching amplifier, voltage amplifier, and power amplifier. For d-c error signals, a chopper is used as shown. The vibrating reed of the chopper is connected through capacitor C_1 to the input stage of the amplifier. As the reed vibrates, the amplifier input circuit is alternately connected to the d-c error voltage and to ground. In this manner, the d-c error voltage is changed to a pulsed or chopped signal that can then be amplified in the R-C and transformer-coupled stages.

The impedance matching amplifier employs an NPN transistor (TR_1) and a PNP transistor (TR_2). Since TR_1 is an NPN unit, its collector load resistor is connected to the positive (ground) side of the supply. The P-type base of this transistor is connected to the positive side of the supply through resistors R_2 and R_6. These resistors, in conjunction with R_1, constitute a voltage divider across the supply and determine the extent to which the P-type base is forward biased. Actually, the base is negative with respect to *ground* but positive with respect to the emitter (which is connected to the negative supply through resistor R_3). The P-type base is therefore positive (less negative) with respect to emitter, and this forward bias places the transistor operating point in the *on* region.

The collector of TR_1 is directly coupled to the base of TR_2. The N-type base of the second stage is connected through R_5 to the negative side of the supply, placing this transistor in the *on* region also. Emitter resistor R_7 stabilizes the circuit with respect to temperature variations. The collector load resistance of the second stage consists of the series combination of R_3 and R_4. Since R_3 is

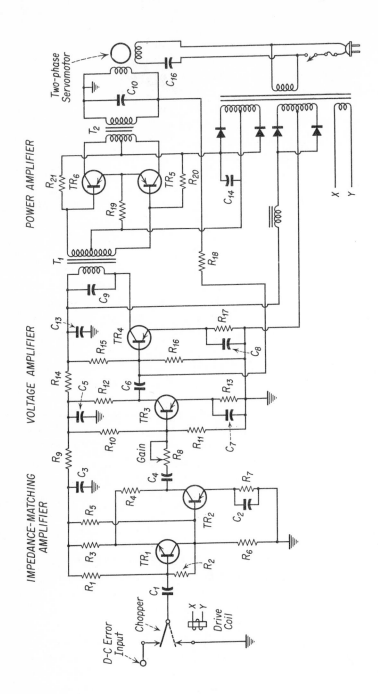

Fig. 7-9 Transistor Amplifier for Electronic Recorder-Controller (Taylor Instrument Co.)

PARTS LIST FOR FIG. 7-9

R_1	1.5 meg	C_1	0.1 μf
R_2	3.9 meg	C_2	100 μf
R_3	2.2K	C_3	100 μf
R_4	3.3K	C_4	100 μf
R_5	5.6K	C_5	50 μf
R_6	2.2K	C_6	100 μf
R_7	4.7K	C_7	100 μf
R_8	50K	C_8	100 μf
R_9	1K	C_9	0.2 μf
R_{10}	18K	C_{10}	1 μf
R_{11}	4.7K	C_{13}	50 μf
R_{12}	4.7K	C_{14}	1000 μf
R_{13}	2.2K	C_{16}	0.05 μf
R_{14}	1.8K		
R_{15}	6.8K		
R_{16}	4.7K	TR_1	2N169
R_{17}	4.7K	TR_2	2N369
R_{18}	1 meg	TR_3	2N369
R_{19}	1.5 Ω	TR_4	2N44
R_{20}	3.3K	TR_5	2N235A
R_{21}	3.3K	TR_6	2N235A

also the emitter resistor of the first stage, a portion of the collector signal of the second stage is fed back to the emitter of the first stage. This negative feedback stabilizes the circuit and also has the effect of raising the input impedance of the amplifier. Without negative feedback, the input impedance would be in the order of several hundred or several thousand ohms; with feedback, the input impedance is raised to over 500,000 ohms. High input impedance is desirable in order to minimize the loading effect of the amplifier on the error detector circuit. As a result of the negative feedback, the voltage gain of the impedance-matching amplifier is only *two*.

Coupling from TR_2 to TR_3 is through capacitor C_4 and variable resistor R_8. This variable, by determining the amount of signal coupled to TR_3, functions as a gain control and is adjusted to eliminate hunting. Transistors TR_3 and TR_4 operate as common-emitter amplifiers. Forward bias for the bases of these two *PNP* transistors is obtained through voltage dividers connected across the negative supply (R_{10} and R_{11} for TR_3, and R_{15} and R_{16} for TR_4). Emitter resistors R_{13} and R_{17} provide temperature stabilization. Gain stabilization is provided by negative feedback from the output transformer (T_2) to the base of transistor TR_4. The primary of transformer T_1 is the collector load of transistor TR_4. Capacitor C_9 tunes the primary of T_1 to approximately 60 cps (the frequency of the chopper). This *tank* circuit responds to the error signal but rejects noise at other frequencies. The secondary of T_1 provides push-pull signals for the output stage.

Fig. 7-10 Transistor Servo Amplifiers (Librascope Division, General Precision, Inc.)

TR_5 and TR_6 are power transistors connected in push-pull to provide greater output power to the control field of the servomotor. Forward bias for the N-type base of each of these transistors is obtained from the negative supply through resistors R_{20} and R_{21}. The control field of the servomotor is tuned by capacitor C_{10}, and power for the main field is obtained from the 60-cycle supply through phase-shifting capacitor C_{16}.

SUMMARY

As in other types of equipment, transistors in servomechanisms offer the advantage of small size, modest power requirements, and resistance to shock and vibration.

In the *NPN* transistor, the emitter and collector are made of *N*-type semiconductor, and a *P*-type base is used. An opposite arrangement is used in the *PNP* transistor. For either type of transistor, the collector junction is reverse-biased and collector current is controlled by the bias of the input junction. Forward bias applied to the input junction will turn the transistor *on* and reverse bias will turn it *off*.

Transistor amplifier circuits are classified as common-base, common-emitter, or common-collector, according to which element is common to both input and output circuits. The common-collector circuit, also known as an emitter follower, is characterized by high input impedance and low output impedance. The common-base circuit has opposite characteristics, and the common-emitter is intermediate between these types.

Interstage coupling of transistor stages may be direct or through transformers or *RC* circuits. Because transistors have relatively low input impedance as compared to vacuum tubes, coupling capacitors are large in value. For the same reason, step-down coupling transformers are employed to effect impedance matches.

Power transistors are used in the output stage of servoamplifiers for driving the error corrector, usually a servomotor. These transistors are mounted on *heat sinks* to conduct heat away from the transistor.

QUESTIONS

1. What is the polarity of the voltage applied to the collector of a *PNP* transistor and of an *NPN* transistor?

2. An *NPN* transistor is connected as a common-emitter amplifier. Will collector current be greater during the positive or negative half-cycle of input signal to the base?

3. What is meant by *thermal runaway*?

4. Explain how an emitter resistor prevents thermal runaway.

5. What is meant by the *alpha* of a transistor?

6. What is the *beta* of a transistor?

7. Draw a diagram of an emitter-follower and explain its operation.

8. Comparing the common-base circuit to the common-collector circuit, which has a higher input impedance and which has a lower output impedance?

9. In which of the three configurations illustrated in Fig. 7-7 is the output signal 180 deg out of phase with the input signal?

10. What is the purpose of a *heat sink*?

Error Amplifiers:
Magnetic

CHAPTER 8

8-1. INTRODUCTION

The magnetic amplifier is electrically and mechanically rugged and provides reliable, long-term service. It is highly immune to shock and vibration; it can be sealed against dirt and moisture; it provides large power gain per stage; and it is instantly ready for use because it requires no warm-up time. Its main disadvantage is the time lag in its response to an input signal. Careful design, however, can minimize this lag. In servomechanism applications, the magnetic amplifier is used either instead of or in conjunction with vacuum tubes or transistors.

8-2. THE SATURABLE REACTOR

Most iron-core inductors (and the circuits in which they are used) are so designed that the core does not saturate during normal operation. If the magnetic core were permitted to saturate, the inductance of the coil would decrease. This decrease occurs because the magnetic flux in a saturated core remains nearly constant and cannot induce counter emf in the coil. The coil therefore loses its ability to *oppose* changes of current flow (decreased inductance).

In the saturable reactor, the core is purposely saturated in order to reduce the amount of inductance. This component therefore functions as a variable inductor: the inductance is controlled by varying the degree of core saturation. In its basic form, the sat-

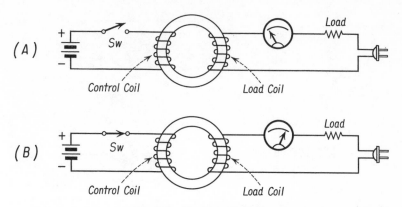

Fig. 8-1 The Saturable Reactor

urable reactor consists of two coils on a magnetic core as shown in Fig. 8-1. A ring-shaped core is shown here, but other shapes may be used instead. The *load* coil of the reactor is connected in series with a load and the a-c source. Current flow through the load is therefore determined by the inductive reactance of the load coil. When the switch is open, as in Fig. 8-1(A), very little current flows through the load because the reactance of the load coil is high. If the switch is now closed, however, as in Fig. 8-1(B), current flow through the load will increase. This increase occurs because the direct current through the control winding causes the core to saturate. The reactance of the load coil therefore decreases and permits a greater flow of current through the load.

Fig. 8-1 illustrates the two extremes: maximum inductive reactance of the load coil (zero current in control coil) and minimum inductive reactance (maximum current in control coil). If a variable resistance is connected in series with the control coil, as shown in Fig. 8-2, the d-c current can be adjusted to saturate the core partially. The inductive reactance of the load coil will now be at some value

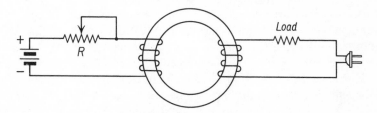

Fig. 8-2 The Magnetic Amplifier

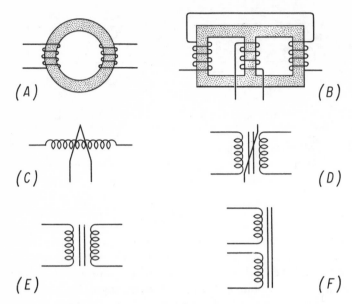

Fig. 8-3 Schematic Symbols for Saturable Reactor

intermediate between minimum and maximum. In this manner the variable resistance in the control circuit can be used to adjust the load current.

Various schematic symbols have been used to represent the saturable reactor. Some of these symbols are shown in Fig. 8-3, including the accepted standard shown at *C*.

8-3. MAGNETIC AMPLIFIERS

The basic circuit shown in Fig. 8-2 has two serious disadvantages.

1. Since the load coil is connected to the a-c source, it functions as a transformer primary and induces voltage in the control coil. The control coil usually consists of many turns of fine wire in order to provide adequate control with relatively small values of direct current. As a result, the transformer action is of the step-up variety and relatively high voltage is induced in the control coil. This voltage may prevent normal operation of the external circuitry connected to the control winding, or may even damage some of the external components. The undesirable transformer action can be

prevented by splitting the load coil into two sections so that the two voltages induced in the control coil will cancel. This technique is employed when the core structure is of the three-leg type shown in Fig. 8-3(B). The same result can be achieved by using two saturable reactors as in Fig. 8-4. The two control coils are connected series-opposing so that the voltage induced in one is canceled by the voltage induced in the other. Alternatively, cancellation of induced voltages can be achieved by connecting the two control coils series-aiding and the two load coils series-opposing.

2. The second disadvantage of the basic circuit shown in Fig. 8-2 is the tendency for the core to desaturate during one half-cycle of the a-c supply voltage. Since alternating current flows through the load coil, only one half-cycle of this current is in a direction that aids the control current in keeping the core saturated. The opposite half-cycle of load current is in a direction that causes desaturation of the core. To prevent this desaturation, a diode is connected in series with the load as shown in Fig. 8-5. The diode permits current flow through the load coil in a direction that aids the control current in saturating the core, but prevents current flow in the opposite direction. Since the load current contributes to the saturation of the core, this circuit is known as a *self-saturating* magnetic amplifier.

Early saturable reactors were constructed with silicon-steel cores similar to those used in transformers. For magnetic amplifier applications, such cores have disadvantages: flux density is relatively low and hysteresis losses are relatively high. Modern units employ nickel-iron alloys and are processed to produce desirable magnetic characteristics. High permeability and grain-oriented alloys are available under such trade names as Permalloy, Mumetal, Orthonol,

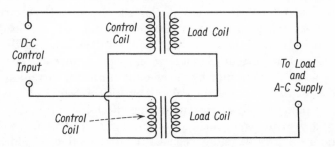

Fig. 8-4 Cancellation of Induced Voltage

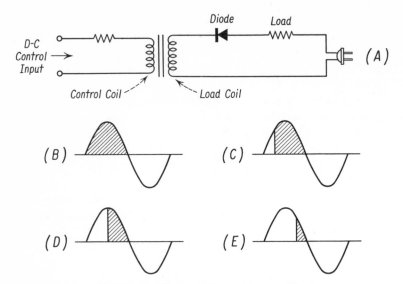

Fig. 8-5 Half-Wave Self-Saturating Amplifier

and Deltamax. Grain orientation is accomplished by cold-rolling and gives the material a *preferred* direction of magnetization. Permalloy and Mumetal are particularly useful for low-level control circuits because saturation is produced at low values of control current. Orthonol and Deltamax are used for higher level applications and have the advantage of greater power-handling capacity for a given core size. Modern core materials are of the *rectangular-loop* variety in which the flux density changes rather abruptly when current flow reaches a critical value. This characteristic is comparable to that of a thyratron: plate current increases abruptly when grid bias is reduced to a critical value.

The value of control current determines the time at which the core will "fire" or saturate during the supply voltage cycle. In Fig. 8-5(A), the diode permits current flow through the load coil only during half of the a-c cycle of supply voltage. During the half-cycle when load current cannot flow, the control current "resets" the flux to a value determined by the amount of control current and the number of turns on the control coil. With this value of flux as a starting point, the load current during the following half-cycle of supply drives the core to complete saturation. The point at which saturation occurs therefore depends upon the value to which the flux was previously reset by the control current. If the control current is large, the core remains at complete saturation during the non-conducting half-cycle in the load circuit. Since the core is already fully saturated, the full half-cycle of supply appears across the load. This is illustrated in Fig. 8-5(B). The shaded area represents the time during which the supply voltage appears across the load.

If the control current is decreased in value, the core will be reset to a lower level of flux (partial saturation) during the non-conducting half-cycle in the load circuit. The conducting half-cycle in the load circuit must then drive the core from partial to complete saturation before the supply voltage can appear across the load. This is illustrated in Fig. 8-5(C). Still smaller values of control current (or even reversed direction of control current) will reset the flux to lesser values (or greater values in the opposite direction). Under these conditions, more time will elapse before the core reaches full saturation; that is, the core "fires" later during the conducting half-cycle in the load circuit. This is illustrated in Figs. 8-5(D) and 8-5(E).

A third coil, known as the *bias* winding, is frequently included on the saturable reactor (see Fig. 8-9). The value of current flow through this winding determines the value of flux to which the core will reset during the nonconducting half-cycle in the load circuit. Bias current is usually in a direction that opposes the effect of the control current. In the absence of control current, the bias current resets the core to negative saturation (saturation in the opposite direction as compared to the direction in which the load current saturates the core). When control current is applied, it opposes the bias current and therefore establishes a new value to which the flux will reset. This combination of bias current and control current can therefore cause resetting to any value of flux between the limits of negative and positive saturation.

Since current can flow through the load only during half of each cycle of a-c supply, the circuit in Fig. 8-5 is *half-wave*. To permit current flow through the load during both half-cycles, two diodes are used as shown in Fig. 8-6. Although this is sometimes referred to as a full-wave circuit, the load current is *not* rectified. For this reason, the circuit is more often referred to as a *doubler*. The dotted and solid arrows in Fig. 8-6 indicate the direction of current flow during both half-cycles of supply. Note that the load current is a-c, but that the current through the load coil during both half-cycles is in a direction that aids core saturation (self-saturating). As in the simpler circuits from which it is derived (Figs. 8-2 and 8-5)

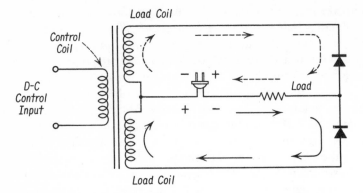

Fig. 8-6 Doubler Magnetic Amplifier

the control current in this circuit saturates the core and therefore reduces the inductive reactance in series with the load.

The circuit in Fig. 8-6 permits control of *alternating current* through the load. If the load is of such nature that it requires direct current, a bridge rectifier may be added to the circuit. An arrangement of this type is shown in Fig. 8-7. The dotted and solid arrows indicate the direction of current flow during both half-cycles of supply voltage. Note that current is in the same direction through the load during both half-cycles, and current through the load coils is always in the direction that maintains core saturation.

The circuit of Fig. 8-7 can be simplified as in Fig. 8-8. Here, only four diodes are required instead of six. Load current is still d-c

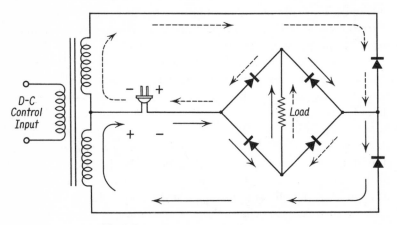

Fig. 8-7 Magnetic Amplifier for D-C Load

however, and the circuit is still self-saturating (current cannot flow through the load coils in a direction that would cause desaturation of the core).

A feedback winding is often included on the saturable reactor, as in Fig. 8-9. This winding is connected in series (or parallel) with the load so that the load current also flows through the feedback coil. The feedback winding can be connected so that it either aids or opposes the effect of the control current. If the feedback current is in a direction that aids the control current, the feedback is positive or regenerative. Under these conditions, a small increase of control current will produce an extremely large increase of load current (the increased load current flows through the feedback winding, further saturating the core, further increasing load current, further increasing feedback current, and so forth). If the connections to the feedback coil are reversed, the feedback will be negative or degenerative. An increase of load current will now produce an increase of feedback current in a direction that tends to reduce saturation of the core. Positive feedback increases gain, and negative feedback improves linearity. The choice of type of feedback is therefore made on the basis of whether gain or linearity is more important in a particular application. A magnetic amplifier employing feedback

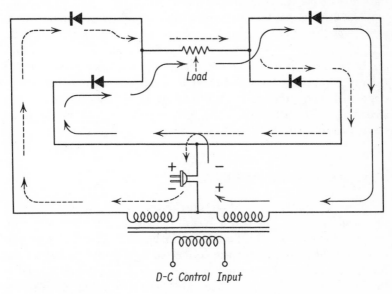

Load

+ −

− +

D-C Control Input

Fig. 8-8   Variation of Magnetic Amplifier for D-C Load

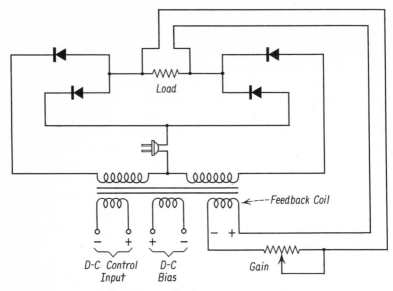

Fig. 8-9   Feedback in Magnetic Amplifier

is shown in Fig. 8-9. The variable resistance in series with the feedback winding determines the magnitude of the feedback current and therefore determines the gain of the circuit.

Like transistor or vacuum tube amplifiers, magnetic amplifier stages can be connected in cascade to provide increased gain. Several stages of the type shown in Fig. 8-8 or Fig. 8-9, for example, can be cascaded by using the control coil of each stage as the load for the preceding stage. A small change of control current in the first stage will then produce a larger change of control current in the second stage, a still larger change of control current in the third stage, and so forth.

8-4. SERVOAMPLIFIERS

A magnetic amplifier controlling a d-c split-field motor is shown in Fig. 8-10. The two halves of the circuit are essentially similar to the magnetic amplifier shown in Fig. 8-7. The armature and forward field of the motor are connected as the load of one of the bridge rectifiers, and the armature and reverse field are connected as the load of the other bridge. Normally (zero-error input) both halves of the circuit conduct equally and the forward and reverse fields are equally energized. Under these conditions, the motor does not rotate.

The control windings are so connected that they oppose the bias windings in one half of the circuit and aid the bias windings in the other half. A d-c error voltage applied to the series-connected control windings will therefore cause one half of the circuit to conduct more (fire earlier in the cycle) and the other half to conduct less (fire later in the cycle). The polarity of the error voltage determines the direction of current flow through the control windings and therefore determines which half of the circuit will conduct more. One polarity of error voltage will therefore produce an increase of current through the forward field and a decrease of current through the reverse field. Error voltage of opposite polarity will produce an opposite effect. For this reason, the motor rotates in a direction determined by the polarity of the input error voltage. As in other position-control servomechanisms, the motor is mechanically coupled to the error-detector circuit to restore it to a condition of balance. The motor stops when it reaches a position determined by the setting of

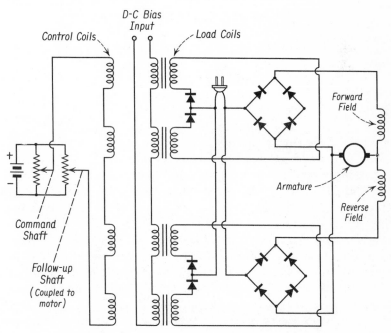

Fig. 8-10 Magnetic Amplifier Control of Split-Field Motor

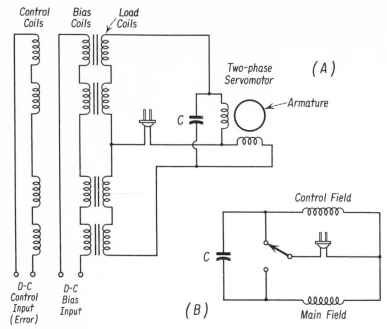

Fig. 8-11 Magnetic Amplifier Control of Two-Phase Servomotor

the command shaft because the error voltage has now been reduced to zero.

A method of controlling a two-phase a-c servomotor is illustrated in Fig. 8-11(A). The d-c bias current is adjusted so that the cores in both halves of the circuit "fire" at 90 deg.

The control coils are so connected that they aid the bias in one half of the circuit and oppose it in the other. The presence of control current therefore causes the cores in one half of the circuit to fire earlier and the cores in the other half to fire later. One half of the circuit therefore turns *on* and the other half turns *off*. As a result, one of the two field windings of the motor is effectively across the a-c input, and the other field is in series with phase-shifting capacitor *C*. An equivalent circuit is shown in Fig. 8-11(B). Here, the double-throw switch represents the two halves of the circuit. With the switch in the position shown, the control field of the motor is across the a-c source, and the capacitor is in series with the main field. If the switch were in the opposite position, the main field would be across the a-c source, and the capacitor would be in series with the control field. The position of the switch therefore determines the direction of rotation of the motor. Likewise, in Fig. 8-11(A), the direction of rotation is determined by which half of the circuit is *on* and which half is *off*. Since this depends upon the direction of current in the series-connected control coils, the polarity of the error voltage determines the direction of rotation of the motor.

Another method of controlling a two-phase servomotor involves the use of the saturable *transformer*. As indicated in Fig. 8-12, the saturable transformer has three windings: primary, secondary, and control. Although the schematic symbol shows the control coil off to one side, it is assumed that all three coils are on the same core. When the switch is open, as in Fig. 8-12(A), normal transformer action takes place. The primary is connected to the a-c source, and voltage is induced in the secondary according to the turns ratio of the transformer. When the switch is closed, however, transformer action is inhibited. Current flow through the control coil magnetizes the core to saturation, and the flux now remains constant at its maximum value. Since the flux does not *vary*, it does not *cut* the turns of the secondary. As a result, no voltage appears in the secondary winding. If a variable resistor is connected in series with the control winding, the control current can be adjusted to produce various degrees of partial saturation of the core. In this manner, secondary voltage can be adjusted to intermediate values.

The use of saturable transformers for controlling a two-phase servomotor is illustrated in Fig. 8-13. With no a-c error signal applied to coupling transformer T_1, triodes V_1 and V_2 conduct

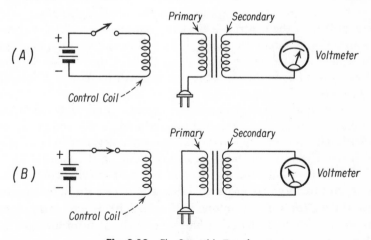

Fig. 8-12 The Saturable Transformer

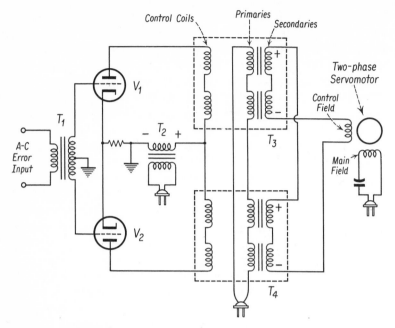

Fig. 8-13 Saturable Transformer Control of Servomotor

equally (during the half-cycles when the excitation supplied by power transformer T_2 has the polarity shown). Since the cores of saturable transformers T_3 and T_4 are saturated partially and equally, the secondary voltages in the two halves of the circuit are equal. Because these secondaries are connected series opposing, the net voltage supplied to the control field of the motor is zero. Under these conditions, the motor does not rotate. The secondary polarities shown are for one half-cycle. During the opposite half-cycle, the polarities will be opposite those shown and will therefore still cancel each other.

Assume now that an a-c error signal is applied to the input terminals of the circuit. The voltage induced in the secondary of T_1 will drive one grid positive and the other negative. The triode which has a positive potential at its grid (during the positive half-cycle of plate supply voltage) will increase its plate current. The triode with the negative grid will, of course, reduce its plate current. Since the d-c control coils in one half of the circuit now carry more current than those in the other half, one of the transformers (T_3 or T_4) becomes more saturated and the other becomes less saturated.

Under these conditions, the secondary voltages of the two halves of the circuit no longer exactly cancel. The *difference* voltage now appears at the control field of the motor, causing the motor to rotate. Note that the polarity of the control field voltage at any given instant depends upon whether T_3 or T_4 produces more output voltage. Since this depends upon which of the two triodes is more conductive, the phase of the error signal determines the direction of rotation of the motor.

A two-stage, push-pull magnetic amplifier is shown in Fig. 8-14. An a-c error signal is supplied by the synchro control transformer which is assumed to be connected to a synchro transmitter. When a difference in angle exists between the rotors of the transmitter and control transformer, an a-c error signal is fed to the demodulator. The d-c output of the demodulator has a polarity and amplitude determined by the direction and amount of angular error of the two rotors. This d-c voltage is applied to the control coils of the first stage of the magnetic amplifier. This stage is a push-pull version of the magnetic amplifier shown in Fig. 8-8.

Since the control coils of the second stage are connected as the loads of the first stage, control current in the second stage is

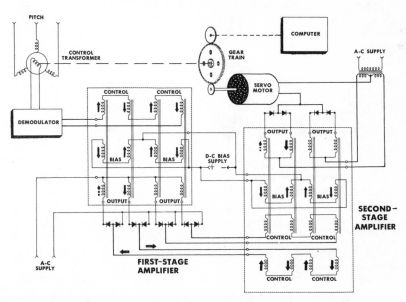

Fig. 8-14 Two-Stage Magnetic Amplifier (Vickers Inc., Division of Sperry Rand Corp.)

Fig. 8-15 Plug-In Magnetic Amplifier (Acromag, Inc.)

greater in value than control current in the first stage. The second stage is a push-pull version of the doubler circuit shown in Fig. 8-6.

The control field of the two-phase servomotor is connected as the load of the second stage. Mechanical coupling from the motor to the shaft of the synchro control transformer brings this rotor into angular correspondence with the rotor of the synchro transmitter. Mechanical coupling from the motor also supplies position information to a computer. This system was designed to calculate the data necessary to describe electrically the pitch of a ship in relation to the earth's magnetic field.

SUMMARY

The magnetic amplifier is electrically and mechanically rugged and provides highly reliable service. Its main component is a saturable core reactor which functions as a variable inductance. Inductance variation is produced as a result of a change in the level of core saturation. Core saturation, in turn, is determined by the amount of current flow through the control coil of the reactor. The current flow through a load connected in series with the reactor can therefore be controlled by varying the current flow through the control coil.

Diodes may be connected in the load circuit in such a way that load current contributes to core saturation. This is the *self-saturating* magnetic amplifier. Additional diodes may be used for rectification if d-c load current is desired. Additional coils may be included on the reactor for bias and feedback purposes. Magnetic amplifiers may be cascaded by using the control coil of one stage as the load of the preceding stage.

In the saturable transformer, current flow through a control coil determines the degree of core saturation and therefore determines the amount of voltage induced in the secondary winding.

QUESTIONS

1. State one advantage and one disadvantage of a magnetic amplifier as compared to a vacuum tube amplifier.

2. If the d-c control current of a saturable reactor is increased in value, will current in the load circuit increase or decrease?

3. What is the purpose of the diode in a self-saturating half-wave magnetic amplifier?

4. In a doubler magnetic amplifier, is load current a-c or d-c?

5. What is the purpose of *bias* current in a magnetic amplifier?

6. Draw a circuit diagram of a three-stage magnetic amplifier using circuits of the type shown in Fig. 8-8.

7. Describe the operation of a saturable transformer under conditions of zero control current and also under conditions of maximum control current.

8. In reference to Fig. 8-13, explain how the servomotor reverses direction when the error signal reverses in phase.

Error Amplifiers: Rotary

CHAPTER 9

9-1. WARD LEONARD SYSTEM

For servomechanism applications involving small or moderate amounts of power, the split-field d-c motor and the two-phase a-c motor are used extensively. For high-power applications, positioning heavy loads for example, large d-c motors are commonly used. The error amplifiers used to control such motors must be capable of supplying large amounts of power. *Rotary amplifiers* are frequently used for this purpose. The Ward Leonard system is representative of this class of machines.

Fig. 9-1 illustrates the basic Ward Leonard system. As shown, the output voltage of the d-c generator is applied as input to the d-c motor. Since the field winding of the motor is excited by a constant d-c source, the speed and direction of the motor are determined by the magnitude and polarity of the voltage applied to its armature. This voltage is produced by the generator. The armature of the generator is driven by a constant-speed motor, and its output voltage is therefore a function of its field current. Because of these relationships, the motor is controlled by the error voltage applied to the field winding of the generator. Assume, for example, that the error voltage has the polarity shown in Fig. 9-1. The resulting flow of current through the field winding of the generator establishes a magnetic field, and the armature of the generator rotates through this field. The voltage induced in the armature has the polarity shown, and this voltage is applied to the armature of the motor. Since both the field and the armature of the motor are energized, the motor rotates.

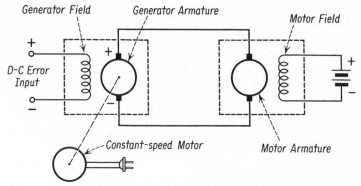

Fig. 9-1   Basic Ward Leonard System

If the polarity of the error voltage had been opposite that shown in Fig. 9-1, the voltage induced in the armature of the generator would also have been reversed in polarity. Since the excitation applied to the armature of the motor would now be opposite that shown, the motor would rotate in the other direction.

The field winding of the generator may be center-tapped to facilitate push-pull operation as shown in Fig. 9-2. Here, the two tubes draw current through the two halves of the field winding. If the plate currents of the two tubes are equal (zero error) the two halves of the field winding are equally energized. The fields therefore cancel and no voltage is induced in the armature of the generator. Since the motor armature receives no excitation, the motor does not rotate.

If an error voltage is applied to the input terminals of the circuit, the grid of one tube will be driven positive and the other grid

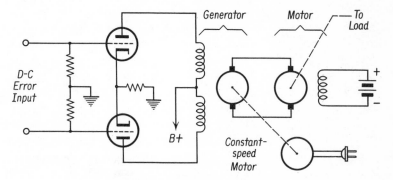

Fig. 9-2   Push-Pull Control of Generator

negative. Current flow through one half of the generator field will now increase, and current through the other half will decrease. The two halves of the field no longer exactly cancel, and voltage is now induced in the armature of the generator. This voltage can be of either polarity, depending upon which of the two tubes draws more current. The direction of rotation of the motor therefore depends upon the polarity of the input error voltage.

The circuit shown in Figs. 9-1 and 9-2 require d-c error voltage. If the error voltage is a-c (from a synchro unit for example) a demodulator circuit may be used to convert it to d-c. Alternatively, a control amplifier of the type shown in Fig. 9-3 may be used.

Assume that an a-c error signal is applied to coupling transformer T_1, and that the polarity in the secondary is as shown. The grid of V_1 is now positive and the grid of V_2 is negative (during the half-cycle of supply when both plates are positive). Tube V_1 therefore draws more current through its half of the generator field, and tube V_2 draws less current through its half. The lack of balance in the two halves of the field winding causes voltage to be induced in the armature of the generator. This voltage, applied to the armature of the motor, causes the motor to rotate. If the input error voltage had been of opposite phase, the grid of V_2 would have been positive during the positive half-cycle of plate voltage. The plate current of V_2 would then be greater than that of V_1. Voltage induced in the generator armature would be opposite, and the motor would rotate in the other direction.

Since the plate supply is a-c, plate current flows only during the positive half-cycle of supply. Plate current is therefore pulsating (half-wave). The resistors and capacitors connected across the

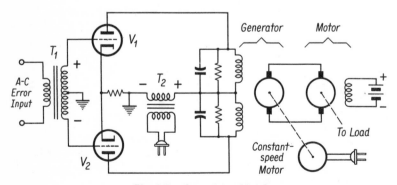

Fig. 9-3 Control Amplifier

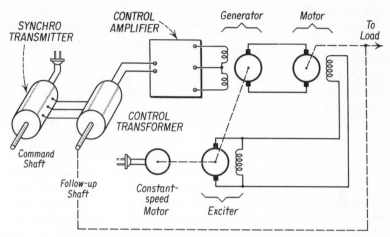

Fig. 9-4 Servomechanism Employing Ward Leonard System

halves of the generator field winding function as filters to smooth out the pulsations of field current.

A servomechanism employing the Ward Leonard system is shown in Fig. 9-4. A synchro transmitter and a synchro control transformer function as the error detector. The control transformer produces an a-c output (error signal) determined by the angular difference between its own rotor and that of the synchro transmitter. This a-c error signal is applied to a control amplifier of the type represented by Fig. 9-3. As a result, one half of the generator field is energized more than the other half. The resulting voltage induced in the generator armature is applied to the motor armature, causing the motor to rotate. The motor now positions the load and also turns the shaft of the synchro control transformer. When this shaft reaches an angular position equivalent to that of the synchro transmitter shaft, the error signal is zero and the motor stops.

The exciter shown in Fig. 9-4 is a d-c generator driven by the constant-speed motor that also drives the main d-c generator. The d-c output of the exciter generator energizes the field of the motor as well as its own field winding.

9-2. RATE SERVOMECHANISMS

Basically, the servomechanism is a position-controlling instrument. With slight modifications, however, it can be used to control the speed rather than the position of the output shaft. Such servomechanisms, known as *rate* or *velocity* servos, generally employ a tachometer to generate voltage proportional to motor speed. The tachometer voltage is applied to an error detector where it is compared against the command input voltage. The difference voltage, if any, is an error signal that corrects motor speed. The speed of the output shaft is therefore determined by the magnitude of the command voltage—for each value of command input there is a corresponding value of motor speed.

Paper, plastics, textiles, and other materials are frequently produced in the form of a long strip that passes in succession through a number of processing machines. Each machine performs a separate operation on the strip, and each has its own individual drive motor. The speed of these motors must be accurately controlled. If one of the machines "pulls in" the strip faster than the preceding machine "pays out" the material, the strip will stretch and break. If one of the drive motors is too slow, the material will pile-up between the machines. This does not imply that all of the machines must be driven at the same speed, only that the speeds of the individual drive motors must be accurately regulated. Pressing of the strip between steel rollers, normal amounts of stretching, and changes of moisture content may produce dimensional changes of the strip. The speed of each machine must therefore be separately controllable and closely regulated. An example of this type of control and regulation is the papermaking mill illustrated in Fig. 9-5.

In the Fourdrinier section, the wet pulp is fed onto a wire-cloth conveyer known as the couch. Here, suction boxes remove much of the water, leaving a mat of wood fibers. The mat then passes through the roller presses where more of the water is removed. In the dryer section, the strip passes over heated rollers, and the moisture content is further reduced. The calender rollers press the paper to the desired finish, and the strip then winds onto a reel.

As shown in Fig. 9-5, a line-powered a-c motor drives the generators (one for each section of the mill). The section motors receive armature excitation from the associated generators, and receive field excitation from an exciter generator driven by the same motor that drives the main generators. A tachometer coupled to each drive motor supplies a rate-dependent voltage to the error detector of each section. In this manner, each motor is servo-regulated to a constant speed. If the speed should attempt to change, the tachometer output

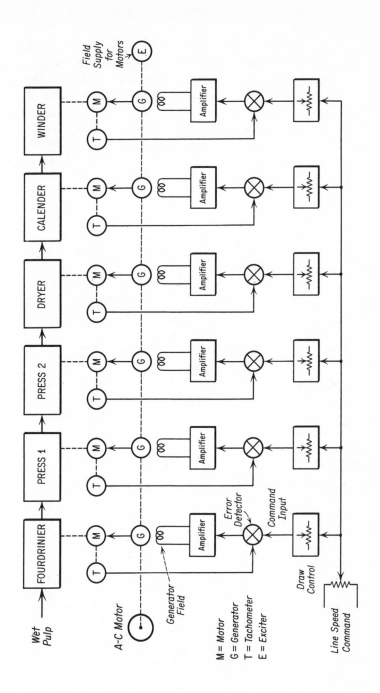

Fig. 9-5 Papermaking Mill

would no longer match the command voltage. The error detector would now supply input to the amplifier, changing the magnitude of generator field current. As a result, the generator output voltage would change, the armature excitation of the motor would change accordingly, and the motor speed would be corrected.

The command voltage for each section can be changed by either the line speed control or by the *draw* control. The draw controls permit individual speed adjustment of each section, and the line control is used to speed up or slow down the entire mill.

9-3. AMPLIDYNE

The use of a d-c generator as an amplifier is illustrated in Fig. 9-6. Input voltage is applied to the generator field winding, and the resulting current flow establishes a magnetic field. The armature, driven by a constant-speed motor, rotates in this magnetic field and is cut by the lines of force. Consequently, voltage is induced in the armature winding, and this voltage is the generator output.

If the input voltage in Fig. 9-6 is increased, a more intense magnetic field will be established. Since the rotating armature is now cut by more flux, more voltage is induced in the armature. The increase of input voltage has therefore produced an increase of output voltage. If a load is connected across the armature, the power developed in this load can be controlled by varying the input power to the field winding. Since a small amount of input power to the field can control a larger amount of load power, the generator functions as an amplifier. Several generations can be cascaded to provide in-

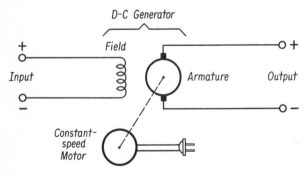

Fig. 9-6 Use of D-C Generator as Amplifier

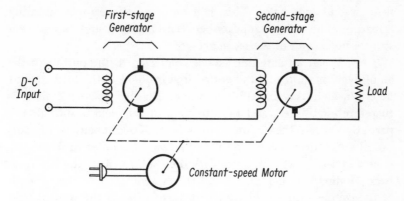

Fig. 9-7 Two-Stage Amplifier

creased amplification. This is illustrated in Fig. 9-7. Here, the armature output of the first stage is applied as input to the field winding of the second stage. A very small change of field current in the first stage can therefore produce a very large change in load current.

The *amplidyne* is a two-stage amplifier combined in a single machine using only one armature. In Fig. 9-8, the d-c input to the control field establishes flux through which the armature rotates (the armature is driven by a separate constant-speed motor). As a result, voltage is induced in the armature winding. This voltage, which appears between brushes A and B, is the output of the first stage. Brushes A and B, however, are shorted together. The short-circuit current is relatively large and establishes an intense magnetic

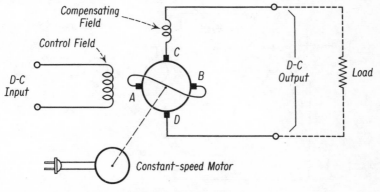

Fig. 9-8 The Amplidyne

field (second-stage field). This field induces voltage in the rotating armature. The voltage appears between brushes *C* and *D*, and constitutes the output of the second stage.

When an external load is connected to the output of the amplidyne, as shown by the dotted line in Fig. 9-8, the load current flows through the armature winding. Another magnetic field is therefore established, and the direction of this field is such that it partially cancels the input control field. To compensate for this cancellation effect, a *compensating winding* is included in the amplidyne and is connected in series with the load. In effect, this is a feedback winding. An increase of load current will increase the strength of the compensating field which, in turn, will aid the control field and further increase load current. A small increase of control input therefore produces a much greater change of load current. Power gains in the range of 5000 to 10,000 are typical.

Only one control field is shown in Fig. 9-8, but several such fields may be available to permit control of the amplidyne by several sources. One of these fields, known as the *reference* field, establishes the output level of the amplidyne. The other control fields then increase or reduce the output according to the error in the system.

An amplidyne type of servomechanism is shown in Fig. 9-9. This is a closed-loop speed-control system which maintains the speed of the d-c motor at a constant value.

The armature voltage for the motor is supplied by the d-c

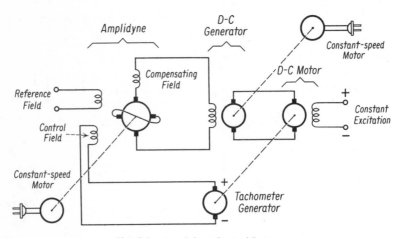

Fig. 9-9 Amplidyne Control System

generator, and the field of this generator is excited by the amplidyne. The amplidyne has two control fields so connected that they oppose each other. Current through the *reference* field establishes the basic speed of the d-c motor. The other control field is energized by a tachometer generator mechanically coupled to the d-c motor. The tachometer is a small d-c generator, and its output voltage is a function of the speed of the d-c motor.

The error-corrective action of the circuit takes place as follows. If the speed of the d-c motor should increase, the tachometer produces more output voltage. The current through the control field of the amplidyne now increases. Since the control field opposes the reference field, the net input to the amplidyne is now less than it was previously. With less input, the amplidyne supplies less output to the field winding of the d-c generator. The output of the generator therefore decreases, reducing the excitation to the armature of the d-c motor. As a result, the d-c motor now reduces its speed to the original value.

SUMMARY

Conventional d-c and a-c servomotors are employed to position light to moderately heavy loads. For control of massive loads, large d-c motors are used. In these applications, the motor is controlled by a generator whose output varies in accordance with the error signal. The Ward Leonard system is typical of this type of control. Here, the error signal controls the direction and magnitude of generator field current. The magnitude and polarity of generator output voltage is therefore a function of the error signal. Since the generator output is applied as armature excitation to the d-c motor, the speed and direction of rotation of the motor are controlled according to the error in the system.

A d-c generator can function as a power amplifier because a small change of field current can produce a large change of generator output. The generator output voltage may be applied as field excitation to a second generator, producing a two-stage generator-amplifier. The amplidyne is an amplifier of this type, the two stages being combined in one machine. Error signal applied to the control field therefore determines amplidyne output voltage. This output then controls the load-positioning d-c motor.

1. In reference to Fig. 9-1, explain how an increase of error voltage produces an increase of motor speed.

2. In reference to Fig. 9-1, explain how a reversal of error polarity produces a reversal of motor direction.

3. During the half-cycle when error voltage is opposite that shown in Fig. 9-3, does tube V_2 conduct? Explain.

4. Assume that *clockwise* rotation of the command shaft in Fig. 9-4 produces *counterclockwise* rotation of the follow-up shaft. State three ways of correcting this defect.

5. What is the purpose of the compensating field in an amplidyne?

6. Assume that the d-c motor in Fig. 9-9 increases its speed because of reduced mechanical loading of its shaft. Explain the circuit action that restores the motor speed to its original value.

Servomechanism Stability

CHAPTER 10

10-1. INTRODUCTION

Ideally, a servomechanism should maintain a condition of zero error regardless of the speed or type of change of the command input. At any and all instants of time, the output should be in exact correspondence with the input. In a practical servomechanism, this ideal can be approached but not fully realized because the corrective action does not occur until an error already exists in the system. The ideal characteristic can be closely approached, however, if the servomechanism has (1) high sensitivity so that it will respond to very small errors, (2) high speed of response so that errors will be rapidly corrected, and (3) stability so that the system will not overshoot or hunt. The last of these requirements is generally the most difficult to satisfy. The other two requirements can be satisfied by the use of (1) a high-gain servoamplifier and (2) a powerful servomotor with a minimum of gear-reduction to the load. This combination of high gain and high speed, however, tends to produce excessive overshoot and instability. In practice, therefore, some degree of sensitivity and speed must be sacrificed in the interests of stability.

One form of instability to which the servomechanism is susceptible is sustained oscillation (hunting). When this type of instability is present, the output shaft swings back and forth through the desired position even when the input shaft is stationary. A common cause of such oscillation is a large time lag in the system. Since a servomechanism cannot respond in zero time to a change of input, the corrective action lags the change of command. As a result of this time lag, the corrective action is still in progress when the error has

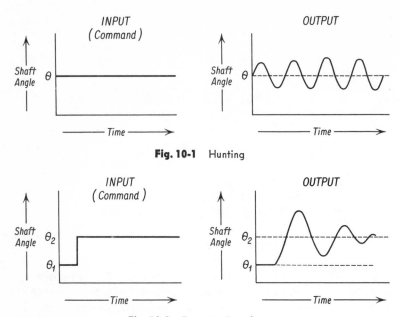

Fig. 10-1 Hunting

Fig. 10-2 Excessive Overshoot

been reduced to zero. The system therefore overcorrects, initiating an opposite correction, overcorrecting again, and so forth. As indicated in Fig. 10-1, the output shaft oscillates around the desired angular position θ.

Another form of instability that is somewhat similar but less severe than hunting is illustrated in Fig. 10-2. If a *step input* is applied to the servomechanism (the command shaft is turned suddenly from angle θ_1 to angle θ_2) the output shaft will vary in position as shown in Fig. 10-2(B). Because of overcorrection, the output shaft turns beyond the desired position θ_2. An opposite correction is therefore initiated and the output shaft reverses. Again, because of overcorrection, the output swings beyond θ_2 (but to a lesser extent than during the previous overshoot). Successive overshoots become smaller and smaller in amplitude, and the output shaft eventually settles at θ_2.

10-2. DAMPING

To prevent excessive overshoot and hunting, *damping* is employed in servomechanisms. Damping may be provided by a mechanical friction device on the output shaft, or the effect of damping can be achieved by electrical means.

The amount of damping employed should be sufficient to prevent excessive overshoot of the type indicated in Fig. 10-2. Too much damping, however, is undesirable because it reduces the speed with which errors are corrected. Various degrees of damping are illustrated in Fig. 10-3. Here, it is assumed that the input shaft has been suddenly turned from θ_1 to θ_2 (step input). Curves *A*, *B*, and *C* represent movement of the output shaft for three different degrees of damping. If the system is slightly *underdamped* (curve *A*), the error will be corrected rapidly but there will be a small amount of overshoot. If the system is *critically damped* (curve *B*), there will be no overshoot but a greater length of time will elapse before the output shaft reaches θ_2. If the system is *overdamped* (curve *C*), the output shaft will approach θ_2 very slowly. Because of this slowness of corrective action, overdamping is undesirable. In practice, slight underdamping is frequently employed: a small amount of overshoot is tolerated in order to achieve rapid correction of error.

Friction devices may be used to achieve the desired degree of damping. A paddle wheel turning in an oil-filled chamber, for example, can be coupled to the output shaft. A disadvantage of this type of damper is that it wastes some of the power of the servomotor, and a more powerful motor is therefore needed than would otherwise be required. Another disadvantage of this type of damper is that it introduces *velocity error*: if the input shaft is turned at a constant rate, the output shaft will follow at a constant rate but will lag the position of the input shaft. These disadvantages are reduced by the use of an *inertia damper*.

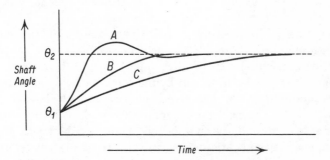

Fig. 10-3 Slight Underdamping, Critical Damping, and Overdamping

The design of an inertia damper is such that friction is minimum when the shaft is rotating at a constant speed. Velocity error is therefore reduced and the output shaft can follow closely a constant velocity rotation of the input shaft. A sudden change of shaft speed, however, will be opposed by increased friction in the inertia damper. This increase of friction prevents excessive overshoot and hunting. One type of inertia damper consists of a metal disc, a felt washer, and a flywheel. The washer is sandwiched between the disc and the flywheel, and the disc is mounted on the motor shaft. When the motor is rotating at a constant speed, the rotary motion is transmitted through the washer from the disc to the flywheel. The flywheel therefore rotates at the same rate as the disc. Because the flywheel is relatively massive, it cannot change its speed suddenly. A rapid change of motor speed will therefore cause the flywheel to slip with respect to the disc. Since the disc and the flywheel are now turning at different rates, the friction of the felt washer opposes the sudden change of motor speed. A spring which adjusts the pressure exerted against the felt washer permits variation of the degree of damping.

Another type of damper which simulates the effect of mechanical friction is the *eddy-current damper*. In one of its forms, the eddy-current damper consists of a copper cup which rotates in a magnetic field. The copper cup is coupled to the motor shaft or output shaft of the servomechanism, and the magnetic field is established by either a permanent magnet or a current-carrying field winding. In either case, rotation of the copper cup through the magnetic field causes eddy currents to be induced in the cup. These currents generate a magnetic field of such polarity that it opposes the rotation of the cup. A retarding force is therefore developed which simulates the effect of viscous friction; that is, the retarding force is proportional to the speed of rotation of the shaft.

In a variation of the eddy-current damper, the permanent magnet is mounted so that it is free to rotate. When the output shaft is rotating at a constant speed, the copper cup and the magnet turn together. Since the cup is not *cut* by the magnetic field, no retarding force is produced. When shaft speed changes suddenly, however, the relatively massive magnet cannot follow the rapid change of speed. As a result of the relative motion of the cup with respect to the magnet, eddy currents are induced in the cup. A drag or retarding force is therefore generated to prevent excessive overshoot and hunting.

The servomotor itself provides some of the damping required in a servomechanism. A friction or eddy-current damper, for example, is often included on the motor shaft inside the housing. The friction of the motor bearings also provides some amount of damping. In addition, the motor produces an electrical damping effect. In the case of a d-c motor, the electrical damping is produced as a result of the voltage induced in the rotating armature as it cuts the lines of force established by the field winding. This voltage is of such polarity that it opposes the armature excitation supplied by the servoamplifier, d-c generator, or amplidyne. Since the opposing voltage induced in the armature is proportional to the speed of rotation of the armature, an effect simulating viscous damping is produced. In the case of an a-c (two-phase) servomotor, the electrical damping effect is a result of the speed-torque characteristic of the motor. In such motors the torque decreases as the speed increases; that is, the motor becomes "less powerful" at higher speeds. Since the load-driving torque falls off at increased speeds, the effect is like that of viscous damping.

10-3. OUTPUT-RATE CONTROL

Feedback is commonly used to provide a damping effect in servomechanisms, reducing the need of mechanical friction to prevent hunting. One such arrangement is shown in Fig. 10-4. The synchro control transformer functions as an error detector to compare the position of the output shaft and the position of the input shaft (represented by the position-defining voltages from the synchro transmitter). According to the difference of position of the input and output shafts, the control transformer supplies an error signal to the amplifier. The amplifier, in turn, controls the amplidyne which provides armature excitation for the load-positioning d-c motor. In addition to the position feedback (mechanical coupling from output to control transformer) the circuit also employs output-rate feedback. The output voltage of the amplidyne—which corresponds to motor speed—is fed back through a high-pass filter to the error amplifier. This feedback is negative, opposing the effect of the error signal and therefore producing a damping effect. If the input shaft is suddenly rotated to a new position, for example, the control transformer will supply an error signal to the amplifier. As a result, the amplidyne supplies voltage to the d-c motor and causes the motor

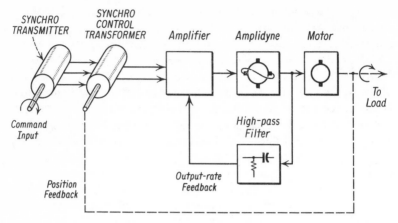

Fig. 10-4 Output-Rate Control

to rotate. The increasing output voltage of the amplidyne, however, is fed back to oppose the effect of the error signal. Since the error signal is effectively reduced, the motor is prevented from accelerating so rapidly that excessive overshoot would result. Output-rate feedback, sometimes referred to as derivative feedback, therefore simulates the effect of an inertia damper: it opposes sudden changes of shaft position.

The high-pass filter in Fig. 10-4 reduces velocity error by preventing feedback when the amplidyne voltage is constant. If the input shaft is rotating at a constant velocity, for example, the output voltage of the amplidyne will remain at a constant value. Since this constant d-c voltage cannot pass through the high-pass filter, no damping effect is produced. The output shaft can therefore closely follow the constant velocity rotation of the input shaft.

Fig. 10-5 illustrates another technique of making corrective action proportional to both the *amount* of error and the *rate of change* of output shaft position. Position feedback is accomplished by means of mechanical coupling from the output shaft to the control transformer. Output-rate feedback is produced by a rate generator. This a-c generator is driven by the servomotor, and its output voltage is proportional to the speed of rotation of its shaft. Excitation for the rate generator is obtained from the same power source that supplies excitation for the synchros. The rate generator output remains constant at the excitation frequency, varies in amplitude according to shaft speed, and reverses in phase when the direction of rotation reverses. The rate signal is fed back in opposition to the error signal from the control transformer. Since a sudden increase of shaft speed produces an increase of output from the rate generator, the error signal is effectively reduced to prevent excessive overshoot.

A disadvantage of the use of an a-c rate generator is that rate feedback occurs even when the servomotor is rotating at constant speed. The resultant damping effect causes the output shaft to lag behind the input shaft (velocity error) when the input is rotating at a constant speed. For this reason a d-c-output rate generator is often used. A system employing a d-c tachometer generator is illustrated in Fig. 10-6. Here again, rate feedback is used in conjunction with position feedback. The d-c output of the generator varies according to shaft speed. Since this rate-dependent voltage is fed back through a differentiator, feedback is prevented by the blocking action of the capacitor when the generator voltage remains constant. The damping effect is therefore eliminated when the output shaft is rotating at a constant speed in response to constant-speed rotation of the input shaft. In this manner, velocity error is reduced. A sudden change of shaft speed, however, will produce a corresponding change of generator output voltage. This change is coupled through the differentiator to a modulator. The modulator, which may be either a vibrating-reed chopper or an electronic equivalent, converts the rate signal to a-c at the frequency of the synchro signal. This rate feedback opposes the error signal from the control transformer and therefore opposes the *sudden* change of output position. In systems employing an error detector whose output is d-c, the modulator shown in Fig. 10-6 would not be required.

The d-c rate generator is mechanically more complex than

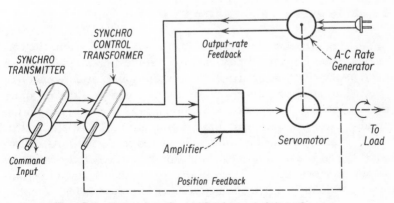

Fig. 10-5   Output-Rate Control Employing A-C Rate Generator

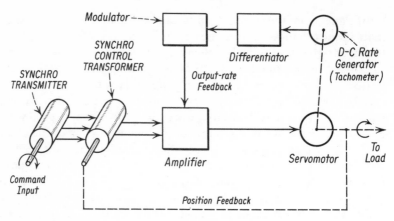

Fig. 10-6 Output-Rate Control Employing D-C Rate Generator

the a-c generator because it requires a commutator and brushes. For the same reason its noise output is greater than that of the a-c generator. It does, however, offer two important advantages over the a-c generator: its output during constant-speed operation can be blocked by a capacitor, and its output is zero when its shaft speed is zero. By contrast, the a-c rate generator produces a small (null) output even when its shaft is stationary. The a-c generator consists of two windings and a solid or cup-shaped rotor. The rotor serves as a coupling medium between the input (excited) winding and the output winding. Frequently d-c generators employ a permanent magnetic, but some models have a field *winding* instead.

10-4. ERROR-RATE CONTROL

In a frequently employed method of stabilization, the corrective action is made proportional to both the amount of error and the rate of change of the error. This form of stabilization, sometimes referred to as *error plus error rate* control, increases the damping effect to prevent the output from approaching its final position too rapidly. Excessive overshoot and hunting are therefore eliminated.

Error-rate stabilization is illustrated in Fig. 10-7. As shown, an *R-C* network is connected between the error detector and the amplifier. When an error exists in the system, the sliders of the command and follow-up potentiometers differ in position. The potential difference between these sliders is the error signal applied to the *R-C* network. Resistors R_1 and R_2 constitute a voltage divider, and the portion of the error signal developed across R_2 is applied to the amplifier. Amplifier input is therefore proportional to the *amount* of error in the system. Capacitor C becomes charged to the voltage across R_1. When the amount of error changes, capacitor C either charges or discharges depending on whether the error has increased or decreased. This charging (or discharging) current produces a voltage drop across R_2. The total voltage across R_2 therefore consists of two components: a component proportional to the amount of error and a component proportional to the rate of change of the error.

An increase of error (when the input shaft is turned to a new position, for example) causes capacitor C to charge. This charging current increases the voltage drop across R_2, resulting in greater input to the amplifier. Corrective action is therefore exaggerated when the system error is increasing. This permits the output to accelerate rapidly. As the output starts to "catch up" to the input, however, the error starts to decrease. Because the output voltage of the error detector now becomes smaller, capacitor C discharges. The discharge current is in a direction that reduces the voltage drop across R_2. Corrective action is therefore diminished as the error approaches zero, preventing excessive overshoot.

From another point of view, the R-C network in Fig. 10-7 can be regarded as a phase shifting network whose output *leads* its input. The leading error signal compensates for the time lags inherent in the servomechanism, improving the stability of the system.

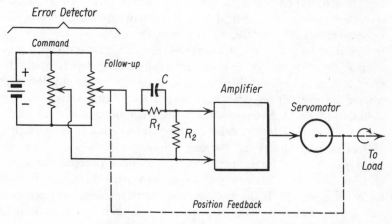

Fig. 10-7   Error Plus Error-Rate Control

(A) 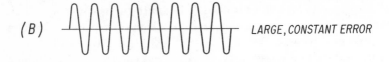 SMALL, CONSTANT ERROR

(B)  LARGE, CONSTANT ERROR

(C) 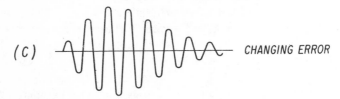 CHANGING ERROR

Fig. 10-8 A-C Error Signals

For this reason the *R-C* network is sometimes referred to as a lead network.

The *R-C* network shown in Fig. 10-7 operates on a d-c error signal. In servomechanisms employing a-c-producing error detectors (synchros or differential transformers, for example) a different form of *R-C* network is required. The error signal shown in Fig. 10-8(A) represents a small, constant error. The sine-wave frequency is equal to the excitation frequency, usually 60, 400, or 1,000 cps. The error signal may be either in phase or 180 deg out of phase with respect to the excitation source, depending upon the direction of the error. Fig. 10-8(B) represents a larger but constant error. In an actual servomechanism, the error does not remain constant (except for velocity error) because the corrective action of the system tends to reduce it to zero. Fig. 10-8(C) is therefore a more typical representation of error signal. During the interval of time represented, the error first increases and then (because of corrective action) decreases toward zero. Error signal is therefore a modulated waveform, the modulation envelope representing the changing amount of error. Such a waveform contains sideband frequencies equally spaced above and below the carrier (excitation) frequency. If the excitation frequency is 400 cps, for example, and the error is changing at a rate corresponding to a frequency of 5 cps, the sideband frequencies will be 395 and 405 cps. If the error changes more rapidly, corresponding to a frequency of 10 cps for example, the sideband frequencies will be 390 and 410 cps.

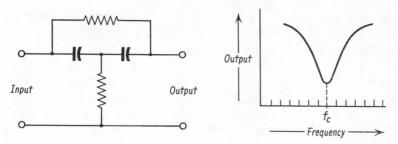

Fig. 10-9   The Bridged-T Network

Since a rapidly changing error produces sideband frequencies farther removed from the carrier or excitation frequency, an *R-C* network of appropriate configuration can be used to produce output proportional to the rate at which the error is changing. A network of this type is shown in Fig. 10-9. The transfer characteristic of this *bridged-T* network is also shown in Fig. 10-9. The values of resistance and capacitance are selected so that the network will produce maximum attenuation at the carrier frequency f_c. Frequencies farther removed from the carrier are attenuated less than frequencies closer to the carrier. A bridged-T network connected between the error detector and the amplifier of a servomechanism will therefore produce more output during rapidly changing error. Since the input to the servoamplifier is greater when error is increasing rapidly, the corrective action is exaggerated to accelerate the output rapidly. As the error begins to decrease, the slowly changing error produces sidebands closer to the carrier. These are attenuated to a greater extent by the bridged-T network so that corrective action is reduced. As a result, the system approaches zero error without a tendency to overshoot excessively.

A *parallel-T* network (Fig. 10-10) may be used instead of

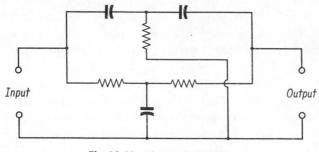

Fig. 10-10   The Parallel-T Network

the bridged-T network. Like the bridged-T, this network produces maximum attenuation at the carrier frequency and progressively less attenuation for sideband frequencies farther removed from the carrier. The output of this network is therefore greater when the servo error is changing rapidly. The parallel-T network consists of a high-pass filter and a low-pass filter in parallel. Sideband frequencies above and below the carrier frequency therefore pass more easily through the high-pass and low-pass filters respectively.

10-5. INTEGRAL CONTROL

The error in a servomechanism must exceed a threshold value before the servomotor will develop sufficient torque to overcome the friction in the system. For this reason, a velocity error occurs: the output shaft lags in position behind the input shaft when the input is rotating at a constant rate. This is true whether the friction is the inherent friction of the servomotor and coupling devices, produced by a mechanical friction device, or simulated electrically. The purpose of integral control is to minimize the velocity error. With this form of control, sometimes referred to as *reset* control, the error signal is proportional to the length of time the error has existed. A long-duration error produces an increase of error signal and therefore exaggerates the corrective action.

Integral control is accomplished by means of an *R-C* network (integrator) connected between the error detector and the servoamplifier. A network of this type is shown in Fig. 10-11. Assuming that an error exists in the system, the error detector will supply input voltage to the integrator circuit. This voltage may be of either polarity depending upon the direction of the error. In either case, the capacitor in Fig. 10-11 will charge toward the value of the error voltage. Input to the servoamplifier therefore increases with time, and corrective action is exaggerated in proportion to the time interval during which the error has existed. Because the output of the integrator increases with time, this type of *R-C* circuit is sometimes referred to as a *lag* network.

In reference to Fig. 10-11, it is assumed that the error detector produces d-c output (a pair of potentiometers across a d-c source, for example). If the error detector is a synchro, differential transformer, or other a-c-output device, a different network is re-

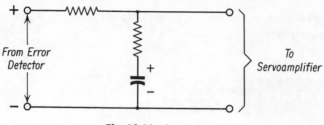

Fig. 10-11 Integrator

quired. Such a network should produce minimum attenuation at the
carrier (excitation) frequency and progressively more attenuation for
sideband frequencies farther from the carrier. A constant or slowly
changing error (sidebands close to carrier) will therefore produce
exaggerated corrective action. The use of such a network, however,
assumes that the excitation frequency does not drift. Such frequency
drift will adversely affect the operation of the servomechanism. For
this reason, it is common practice to rectify the a-c error signal and
to apply the resultant d-c to a network such as that shown in Fig.
10-11. A modulator may then be used to reconvert the error signal to
a-c for the servoamplifier.

Integral control is most effective for constant or slowly
changing errors. Rapidly changing errors are "ignored" by the integrator because the capacitor charge remains practically constant
during such changes; that is, the time constant will not permit the
capacitor to charge and discharge as rapidly as the error changes.
Integral control therefore complements error-rate control, and the
two are often used in combination. Error-rate control stabilizes the
servomechanism with respect to sudden changes of error, and integral control reduces steady-state or velocity error. A combination
error-rate and integrator network is shown in Fig. 10-12. The use of

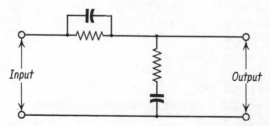

Fig. 10-12 RC Network for Combination Error-Rate
and Integral Control

these two forms of control, in addition to some viscous friction, leads to a highly stable system.

SUMMARY

Stabilizing techniques are employed in the servomechanism to permit an increase of amplifier gain (greater sensitivity) without introducing hunting. Friction or eddy-current dampers or both are employed to prevent excessive overshoot. Such dampers, however, reduce the speed of correction and also introduce velocity error.

Output-rate control produces a damping effect that increases in proportion to the rate of change of the output shaft. A rate-dependent voltage can be generated by either an a-c or a d-c generator driven by the servomotor. With a d-c generator, a blocking capacitor can be used to reduce the damping effect during constant-speed rotation.

Error-rate control makes the corrective action proportional to the rate of change of the error. An increasing error speeds up the corrective action, and a decreasing error slows it down to prevent excessive overshoot. Integral control reduces steady-state velocity error by making corrective action proportional to the length of time the error exists. Error-rate control and integral control are frequently used in combination.

QUESTIONS

1. What is the advantage of slight underdamping of a servomechanism as compared to critical damping?

2. What is meant by "hunting"?

3. Name two disadvantages of the use of a friction device such as a paddle wheel in an oil chamber.

4. Define *viscous damping*.

5. State one advantage of the a-c rate generator as compared to the d-c generator.

6. State one advantage of the d-c rate generator as compared to the a-c generator.

7. Explain the purpose of the "blocking capacitor" used with a d-c rate generator.

8. Compare the effects of output-rate control and error-rate control during a rapidly increasing error.

9. In reference to an a-c-producing error detector such as a synchro, describe the relationship between carrier frequency, sideband frequencies, and rate of change or error.

10. What is the advantage of the use of integral control?

Applications

CHAPTER 11

11-1. INTRODUCTION

Servomechanism techniques are used extensively in industry for measuring, recording, and controlling process variables such as temperature, pressure, flow rate, tension, position, speed, and so forth. For some applications, the equipment is designed to record the value of the variable; for other applications, the equipment *controls* as well as records. Recording is usually accomplished by

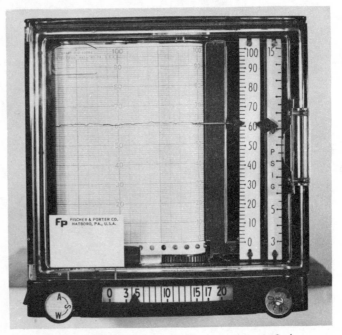

Fig. 11-1   Industrial Recorder (Fischer and Porter Co.)

means of a lightweight pen which traces a line on a moving strip of paper. This trace is a graph showing the variable plotted as a function of time. An industrial recording control station is shown in Fig. 11-1. The controlled variable is indicated and recorded on a 4-in. strip chart. An additional recording pen for a separate or a related process variable is available on two-pen models.

Electronic recorders, variously referred to as self-balancing recorders, strip-chart potentiometers, and null-seeking recorders, vary in circuit details but employ the same basic principle. By means of an appropriate transducer, the process variable is converted to an electrical signal (either a-c or d-c). This signal is then compared to a reference and the difference (error) is applied to an amplifier. The amplified error signal then drives a correcting device such as a servomotor. Through mechanical linkages, the servomotor rebalances the circuit. A typical arrangement is shown in Fig. 11-2. The unknown voltage (d-c in this case) is applied series-opposing with respect to a

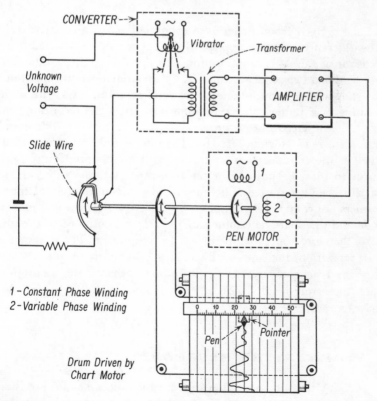

Fig. 11-2 Recording Potentiometer (Daystrom Inc., Weston Instruments Division)

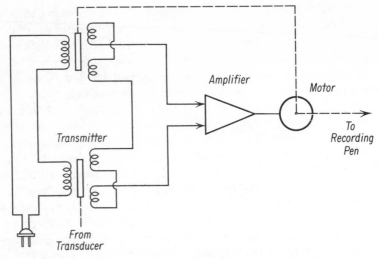

Fig. 11-3 Recorder Employing Differential Transformers

voltage derived from a slide-wire connected across a standard cell. The difference voltage is applied to a chopper and is converted to an a-c error signal. After amplification, this signal is applied to the control field of a two-phase servomotor. The servomotor now repositions the slide-wire to reduce the error to zero. By means of a wire cable running over pulleys, the servomotor also drives the recording pen.

An electronic recorder employing a pair of differential transformers is shown in Fig. 11-3. The differential transformer identified as the *transmitter* is controlled by a motion-producing transducer so that the position of the core represents the value of the variable being recorded. The outputs of the two differential transformers are connected in opposition. An error signal whose magnitude and phase are determined by the relative positions of the two cores therefore appears at the input of the amplifier. The servomotor now repositions the core to which it is mechanically coupled. When this core reaches a position corresponding to that of the transmitter core, the error signal is zero and the motor stops. The motor also drives a recording pen.

11-2. PRESSURE RECORDER

A pressure-measuring instrument combining the precision of a liquid manometer with the flexibility of a servomechanism has been developed by the *Exactel Instrument Co.* The basic principle of operation is illustrated in Fig. 11-4. A float, positioned by the mercury column in a manometer tube, is coupled to the armature (core) of a differential transformer. When the armature is centered with respect to the two series-opposing secondaries of the differential transformer, the secondary voltages exactly cancel and there is no input to the servoamplifier. Under these conditions, the servomotor does not rotate. When the pressure changes however, the height of the mercury column changes accordingly and the armature moves away from its center position. Since the voltages induced in the two secondaries are no longer equal, the difference voltage appears as input to the servoamplifier. The phase of this error signal depends upon the direction in which the armature has moved (up or down). In one case, the error signal will be in phase with the excitation applied to the primary winding; in the other case, the error will be 180 deg out of phase with the excitation. The amplified error signal drives the servomotor in a direction determined by the direction in which the armature has moved. The servomotor now raises or lowers the case of the differential transformer until the secondaries are balanced; that is, until the armature is again centered with respect to the two secondaries. At this time the secondary voltages again exactly cancel, there is no input to the servoamplifier, and the motor stops. The position of the servomotor shaft is therefore a measure of the

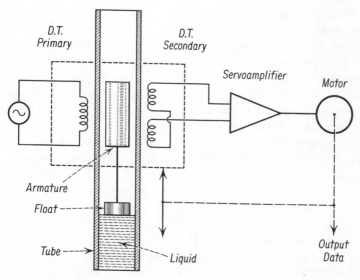

Fig. 11-4 Pressure-Measuring Servomechanism (Exactel Instrument Co.)

pressure represented by the height of the mercury column. A number-wheel counter (similar to the mileage indicator of an automobile) may be coupled to the servomotor shaft to provide a numerical display of the value of the pressure. For *remote* indication, the motor shaft may be coupled to a synchro transmitter. A remotely located synchro receiver then drives the number-wheel counter to indicate the pressure. Various accessories are available for use with the basic instrument: (1) an automatic temperature compensating device that feeds a correction signal to the servoamplifier so that pressure readings are not affected by temperature changes, (2) stainless steel manometer tube for high-pressure applications and for extension of range and safety, (3) floats for liquids other than mercury, (4) calibrating checking devices, (5) analog to digital converters, and others.

11-3. WEIGHT MEASUREMENT

The measurement of the weight of heavy equipment such as railroad cars, loaded trucks, industrial machinery, and so forth, is usually accomplished by means of load cells. The load cell contains one or more columns of steel to support the weight to be measured. Under such load, the steel columns are compressed and therefore shorten very slightly. The problem then becomes one of measuring the amount of shortening of the columns. For this purpose, one or more strain gauges are attached to the columns in such a way that some of the gauge wires are stretched and others are compressed. When the resistance wire in the strain gauge is stretched, it becomes longer and thinner and its resistance increases. When compressed, the wire becomes shorter and thicker and its resistance decreases. The strain gauge wires are connected as a bridge circuit. The load cells may be mounted under a weighing platform, or they may be connected to a cable used to lift the weight to be measured. In either case, the strain-gauge bridge becomes unbalanced and produces an output signal.

As indicated in Fig. 11-5, the bridge is excited by an a-c source. Bridge output is therefore a sine-wave whose amplitude represents the weight being measured. The output of the bridge is cancelled by a sine-wave of opposite phase derived from the balancing potentiometer. In the event that exact balance does not exist, a difference voltage appears at the input of the amplifier. As a result, the servomotor rotates and drives the balance potentiometer. When

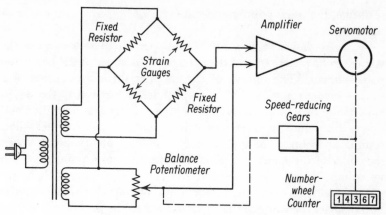

Fig. 11-5 Electronic Weighing System

the slider of the potentiometer reaches a point at which its voltage exactly cancels the bridge output, the error signal is zero and the motor stops. The motor is coupled to a number-wheel counter to indicate weight, or to a pointer that moves over a calibrated scale.

11-4. SERVO-TYPE VOLTMETER

A voltmeter featuring numerical readout by means of a number-wheel counter is illustrated in Fig. 11-6. This is easier to

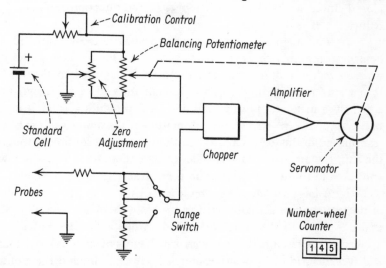

Fig. 11-6 Servo-Type Voltmeter

read than the usual pointer-and-scale type of indicator and is free of parallax error.

As shown in Fig. 11-6, a chopper alternately samples the voltage to be measured and the voltage at the slider of the balancing potentiometer. The output of the chopper therefore consists of a square-wave error signal whose amplitude corresponds to the difference of the two sampled voltages. This error signal is amplified and drives a servomotor. The motor is coupled to the number-wheel counter and also to the shaft of the balancing potentiometer. When the slider of the balancing potentiometer reaches a point at which its voltage equals the voltage at the tap of the range switch, the error signal is zero and the motor stops. The number-wheel counter now displays the value of the input voltage to the probes.

11-5. MAGNETIC-CLUTCH SERVO

In a variation of the basic servo technique, the motor is allowed to rotate continuously. The motor is coupled to the load through a pair of magnetic clutches, both of which are de-energized when error in the system is zero. When an error exists, one clutch or the other will energize and torque is transmitted to the load. The direction of the error determines which of the two clutches will energize and therefore determines the direction in which the load is moved. In either case, the load moves in the direction required to reduce the error to zero.

The magnetic clutch consists of two circular plates in a housing containing magnetic particles in oil. One of these plates is coupled to the motor shaft and the other is coupled to the load. When current is allowed to flow through the coil of the magnetic clutch, the magnetic powder solidifies and provides a solid bridge between the two plates. The rotary motion of the motor shaft is now transmitted to the load shaft. When there is no current flow through the coil, the magnetic powder is *loose*. The motor-driven plate now continues to rotate but the motion is not transmitted to the load.

A basic clutch drive circuit is shown in Fig. 11-7. The coils of the two clutches are connected in the plate circuits of two tubes so that one clutch or the other will energize when a d-c error voltage is applied to the circuit. When the error voltage is of such polarity that it drives the grid of V_1 positive, clutch 1 will energize and the motor

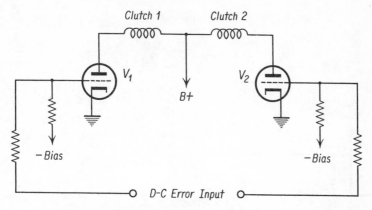

Fig. 11-7 Clutch Drive Circuit

will drive the load. For error voltage of opposite polarity, clutch 2 will energize and the load will be driven in the opposite direction.

A clutch-type servomechanism for remote positioning applications is shown in Fig. 11-8. The motor and clutch assembly is shown at the top, and the servo amplifier is below. A functional diagram of this system is shown in Fig. 11-9. The output shaft follows

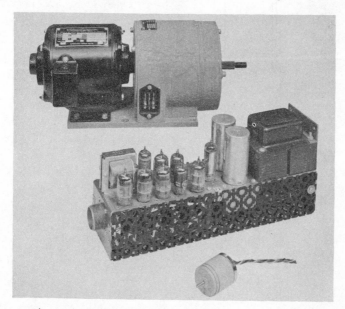

Fig. 11-8 Servomechanism for Remote Positioning Applications (Lear, Inc.)

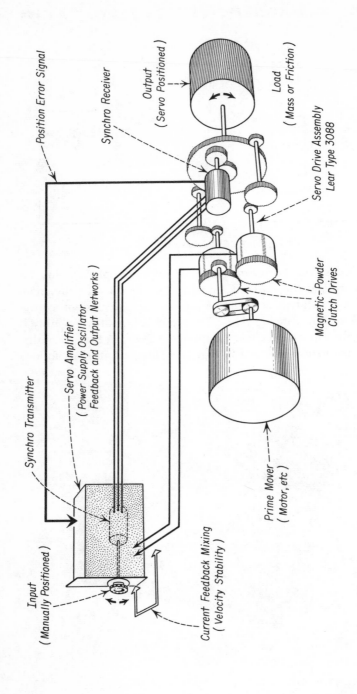

Fig. 11-9 Functional Diagram of Clutch-Type Servo (Lear, Inc.)

movements of the manual control with exceptional speed and accuracy. The system reaches maximum speed within one-fiftieth of a second and is accurate within one-fourth of one degree.

11-6. RADIO DIRECTION INDICATOR

Navigational devices, automatic flight controls, and missile guidance systems frequently employ servomechanism techniques. An example, an automatic direction finder, is shown in Fig. 11-10. The indicator of this instrument displays the flight direction of the aircraft in which it is installed with respect to the radio station to which it is tuned. Acting on this information, the pilot guides the aircraft to the desired destination.

The two loop antennas are wound at right angles to each other on a flat ferrite core. These loops are connected to the two stator coils of a *resolver*. The resolver, which resembles a synchro unit in appearance, is shown schematically in Fig. 11-11. The two stator coils function as transformer primaries and induce voltage in the rotor which functions as a secondary. As indicated, the stator coils are positioned at right angles to each other. One stator therefore induces voltage in the rotor proportional to the sine of the shaft angle, and the other stator induces voltage proportional to the cosine of the shaft angle. The net voltage induced in the rotor is therefore the vector sum of the two input voltages to the stators.

In Fig. 11-10, the amplitudes of the signals in the two loop antennas are determined by the orientation of the aircraft with respect to the transmitting station. These two signals are applied to the two stator windings of the resolver. The voltage induced in the rotor is therefore a function of the direction of flight with respect to the location of the transmiter. The rotor voltage is applied as an error signal to the receiver, and the output of the receiver drives a servomotor. Through a speed-reducing gear, the motor is coupled to the rotor shaft of the resolver and also to the pointer of the indicator. When the rotor of the resolver reaches a position in which the voltages induced in it by the two stators are equal and opposite, the error signal is zero. The servomotor now stops rotating, and the indicator displays flight direction in terms of transmitter direction.

As shown, the servomotor is coupled to the shaft of a synchro transmitter. This transmitter may be connected to one or more remotely located synchro receivers. These receivers will position their

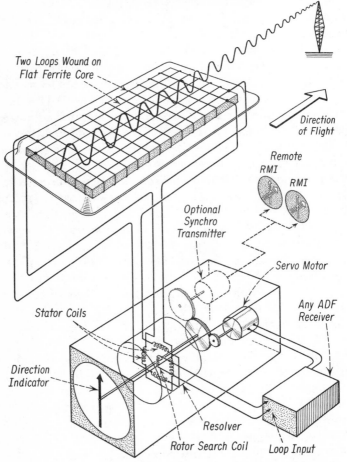

Fig. 11-10 Automatic Direction Finder (Lear, Inc.)

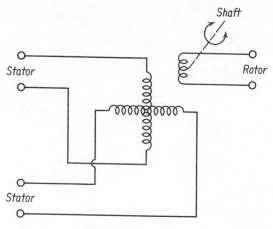

Fig. 11-11   The Resolver

.shafts to correspond to the shaft position of the synchro transmitter. Pointers attached to the receiver shafts therefore repeat the reading of the main indicator. In this way, radio magnetic indicators (RMI) can be installed at several locations in the aircraft.

11-7. AUTOMATIC FLIGHT CONTROL

Automatic flight controls, whether for aircraft or missiles, are load-positioning servomechanisms in which the load is the aircraft or missile itself. Such positioning directs the aircraft or missile toward a specific destination or target. The command input signals for these servomechanisms may be derived from radio or radar signals, from computers, or from transducers such as star-tracking photocells, heat-sensing elements, attitude-sensing gyroscopes, or acceleration-responsive devices. In any case, the error signal must eventually control an error-correcting device to correct deviations from the desired flight path. The correcting device may be electrical, pneumatic, hydraulic, or combinations of these types.

Fig. 11-12 shows the corrector components of an aircraft rudder control system. The motor rotates continuously and torque is transmitted to the rudder cable capstan by means of powdered-iron magnetic clutches. In this system, a gyroscope detects deviations from the desired heading and produces a corresponding error signal. The error amplifier then energizes either the right-turn or the left-turn

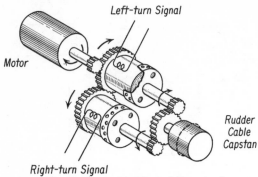

Fig. 11-12 Rudder Control (Lear, Inc.)

clutch, positioning the rudder to return the aircraft to the correct heading.

Some automatic flight control systems make use of altitude controllers for fixed-altitude flying or for use in conjunction with instrument landing equipment. Two techniques of sensing altitude

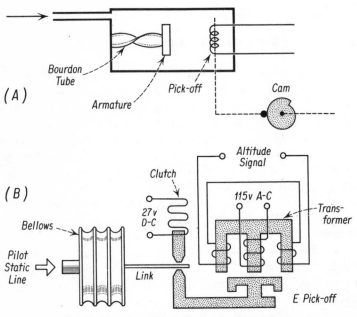

Fig. 11-13 Altitude Sensing (A—Servomechanisms Inc.;
B—Sperry Gyroscope Co.)

changes are illustrated in Fig. 11-13. In Fig. 11-13(A), a twisted Bourdon tube responds to changes of air pressure which accompany changes of altitude. The Bourdon tube controls the position of an armature (core) with respect to an inductive pick-off. The pick-off element, an *E*-type differential transformer, supplies an output (error) signal to an error amplifier. Magnetic clutches, responding to the error signal, position the elevator surfaces of the aircraft to maintain the desired altitude.

In Fig. 11-13(B), a spring-opposed bellows senses air pressure changes corresponding to deviations from the desired altitude. Motion of the bellows is transmitted through a link to the armature of an *E* transformer. The series-opposed secondaries of the transformer therefore produce an altitude-error signal.

As indicated in Fig. 11-13(B), a clutch is used to establish mechanical coupling between the bellows link and the armature of the *E* transformer. When the clutch is not energized, the armature of the transformer remains in its center position. As a result, the error signal will be zero at the altitude at which the altitude-control is turned on.

11-8. HYDRAULIC AND PNEUMATIC CONTROLS

Electro-hydraulic error correctors are used extensively in automatic guidance systems. The basic technique is illustrated in Fig. 11-14. Here, the position of the spool of the transfer valve is controlled by a pair of solenoids. When system error is zero, both solenoids are de-energized and the valve is *closed*. This is illustrated in Fig. 11-14(A). The center section of the spool blocks the inlet so that oil cannot pass into the transfer valve.

If the solenoid at the left is energized (in response to an error signal) the spool moves to the left as shown in Fig. 11-14(B). Oil, under pressure, is now forced through the transfer valve in the direction indicated by the solid arrows. The oil entering the right-hand chamber of the actuator forces the piston toward the left. As a result, the oil in the left-hand chamber of the actuator is forced back to the return line as indicated by the dotted arrows. The piston of the actuator is mechanically linked to the control surfaces of the aircraft or missile, correcting the flight attitude. The error signal is

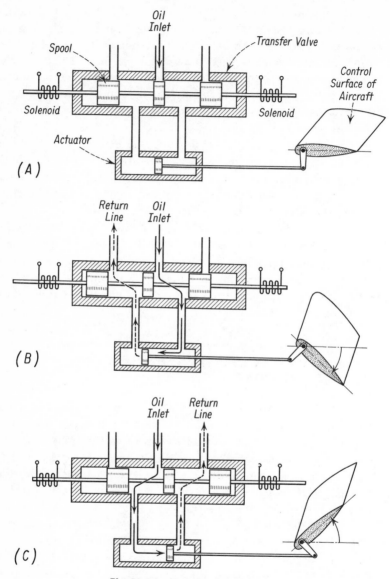

Fig. 11-14 Hydraulic Control System

now zero, the solenoid de-energizes, and a spring returns the valve spool to its center position.

If the error had been in the opposite direction, the right-hand solenoid would be energized. The spool of the transfer valve would now move toward the right as shown in Fig. 11-14(C). Oil is

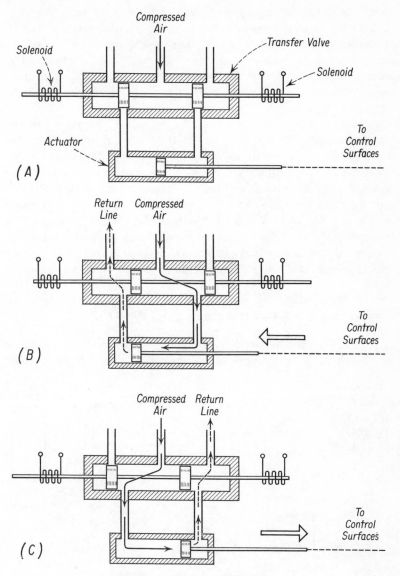

Fig. 11-15 Pneumatic Control System

forced through the valve and into the left-hand chamber of the actuator as shown by the solid arrows. The piston of the actuator moves toward the right, and oil from the right-hand chamber is forced back to the return line as indicated by the dotted arrows.

Compressed air may be used instead of oil to drive the

piston of the actuator. A *pneumatic* system of this type is shown in Fig. 11-15. As in the case of the hydraulic transfer valve, a pair of solenoids permits positioning of the spool in one direction or the other (depending upon the direction of error in the system). The compressed air enters the actuator unit and moves the piston. This motion is transferred to the control surfaces to correct the flight attitude.

Reference has been made in preceding paragraphs to the control surfaces of an aircraft or missile. Such surfaces include rudders, elevators, and ailerons which, by protruding into the airstream, alter the attitude of the craft. Above the atmosphere, however, these control surfaces become ineffective. Missile direction and attitude are therefore controlled by other means such as (1) deflector vanes which can be positioned in the path of the exhaust gases and (2) gimbal-mounted engines that can be positioned to change the direction of thrust. Control systems basically similar to those already described are used for positioning the deflection vanes and gimbals.

11-9. ROCKET-THRUST CONTROL

The control system shown in Fig. 11-16 maintains the thrust level of a liquid propellent rocket engine at a specific magnitude.

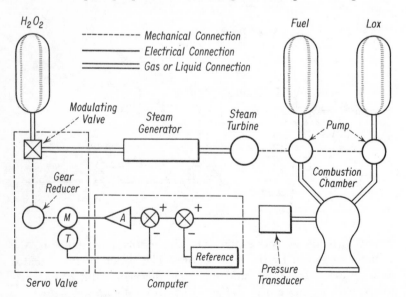

Fig. 11-16 Rocket Thrust Control (Servomechanisms Inc.)

Fuel and liquid oxygen are pumped into the combustion chamber by a pair of pumps driven by a steam turbine. A servo valve controls the flow of hydrogen peroxide (H_2O_2) into the steam generator and therefore determines the rpm of the pumps.

Pressure in the combustion chamber is sensed by a transducer, and the transducer output is compared against a reference. The error signal is amplified and applied to a two-phase servomotor. Through a reducing gear, the motor adjusts the valve to restore chamber pressure to the correct value. A tachometer driven by the servomotor provides feedback for output-rate control.

11-10. COMPUTER SERVOS

Servomechanisms are frequently employed in analog computers and in analog-to-digital converters. An example is shown in Fig. 11-17. The servo *multiplier* accepts two input voltages (E_X and E_Y) and produces output voltage (E_{XY}) proportional to the product of $E_X \times E_Y$. Voltage E_Y is the command input to the servomechanism. The servomotor rotates until the voltage from the follow-up potentiometer matches voltage E_Y. Potentiometer R_1 is also driven by the servomotor, and the slider of this potentiometer therefore assumes a position determined by E_Y.

The magnitude of the voltage appearing at the slider of R_1 depends upon (1) the magnitude of voltage E_X and (2) the position of the slider. Since this slider is positioned according to the value of E_Y, the output voltage represents the product of the two input voltages.

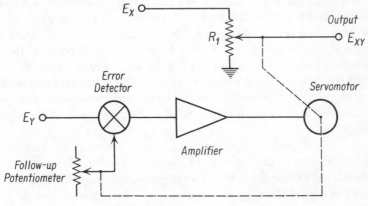

Fig. 11-17 The Servo Multiplier

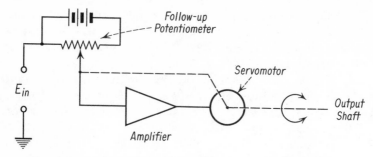

Fig. 11-18 Servo for Converting Voltage-Level Data to Shaft-Position Data

A *rate* servo differs from a *position* servo in that the command input voltage determines the speed rather than the position of the output shaft. In this type of servo, the error detector compares the command input against a voltage representing the rate of the output. A tachometer generator driven by the servomotor, for example, supplies a rate-dependent voltage to the error detector. A given magnitude of command voltage therefore causes the motor to rotate at a corresponding speed.

The rate servo can perform the mathematical operation of integration. Because the total travel of the output shaft depends upon (1) the magnitude of the command voltage and (2) the length of time this voltage is applied, the servo output represents the time integral of the input.

In an analog computer, data are represented by voltage levels or by shaft angles. A particular numerical value, for example, can be represented by a voltage of corresponding magnitude or by a rotary shaft positioned to a corresponding angle. It is sometimes necessary to convert voltage-level data to shaft-position data. A servomechanism for performing such conversion is shown in Fig. 11-18. The input voltage to be converted to a corresponding shaft angle is balanced by the voltage from the follow-up potentiometer. If these voltages do not match, the difference appears as error input to the amplifier. The servomotor now adjusts the follow-up potentiometer to establish a condition of balance. The angular displacement of the output shaft is therefore representative of the magnitude of the input voltage.

In digital equipment data are represented by two-state (on-off) devices. Information to be handled in a digital system must therefore be converted from its analog form (voltage level or shaft angle) to digital form. Such conversion can be accomplished by at-

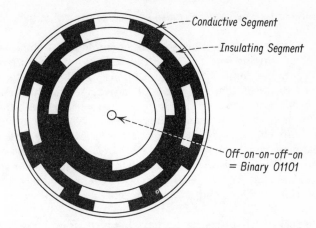

Fig. 11-19   Disc Encoder

taching a disc encoder to the output shaft in Fig. 11-18. A disc of this type is shown in Fig. 11-19. As indicated, the disc has concentric rings made up of conductive and nonconductive segments. Electrical contact with the disc is established by means of a set of wipers or brushes, one for each ring. According to the angular displacement of the disc, some of the brushes rest on conducting segments and others on nonconducting segments. Those brushes which contact conducting segments correspond to closed switches, and those on insulating segments represent open switches. Shaft-angle data is therefore converted to on-off (binary) data suitable for digital processing. Some disc encoders employ transparent and opaque segments instead of conductive and insulating segments. Such discs employ light beams and photocells instead of brushes.

SUMMARY

Servomechanisms are used industrially for automatic control and recording of process variables. By means of an appropriate transducer (thermocouple, bellows-controlled differential transformer, and so forth) process variables such as temperature and pressure are converted to corresponding electrical signals. These signals are compared to a reference or command signal, and the difference voltage (error) is applied to the servoamplifier. The servomotor drives a recording pen and may also be used to control valves, pumps, and so forth.

Magnetic clutches are sometimes employed to eliminate the necessity of starting and stopping the servomotor. In such servomechanisms, the motor rotates continuously and torque is transmitted to the load through either of two magnetic clutches. One clutch, when energized, drives the load in one direction, and the other clutch drives it in the opposite direction. When the servo error is zero, both clutches are de-energized and the load is stationary. The magnetic clutch consists of two discs in a solution of powdered iron in oil. One disc is driven by the motor and the other is connected to the load. When the clutch coil is energized, the powdered iron solution solidifies and provides mechanical coupling between the discs.

Servomechanisms are employed in aircraft and missile flight control systems. In the radio magnetic indicator, the error signal is derived from the incoming radio signal. The servomotor controls a pointer to indicate the direction of the radio transmitter with respect to the heading of the aircraft. Servomechanisms responding to air pressure variations are used in altitude indicating and controlling systems.

Hydraulic and pneumatic actuators are commonly employed in automatic flight control systems. These actuators, responding to servo errors, position the flight control surfaces, deflector vanes, rocket motors, and so forth.

QUESTIONS

1. Describe a motion-producing transducer that could be used to position the core of the transmitter in Fig. 11-3.
2. Describe the construction and purpose of a load cell.
3. Explain how a *calibration* control can be added to the circuit in Fig. 11-5.
4. Explain how a *zero* control can be added to the circuit in Fig. 11-5.
5. Describe several methods of preventing overshoot and hunting in the circuit in Fig. 11-6.
6. In reference to Fig. 11-6, what modifications are required to permit measurement of a-c as well as d-c voltages?
7. Describe the construction and explain the operation of a resolver.

8. What is the purpose of a hydraulic transfer valve?

9. What is the purpose of a hydraulic actuator?

10. What is the advantage of the hydraulic system in Fig. 11-14 as compared to using the solenoids to position the control surfaces directly?

11. What is the difference between a *hydraulic* system and a *pneumatic* system?

12. Sketch and explain a control system that will reduce rocket thrust as altitude increases.

INDEX

INDEX